The  POCKETGuide
BARCELONA

Barcelona: Regions and Best places to see

⭐ Best places to see 20–41

🔲 Featured sight

Las Ramblas and around 45–60

La Ribera to Port Olímpic 61–68

The Eixample and Gràcia 69–80

Montjuïc to Sants 81–86

Pedralbes and Tibidabo 87–91

Original text by Teresa Fisher

Updated by Josephine Quintero

© AA Media Limited 2008
First published 2008. Reprinted May 2010

ISBN: 978-0-7495-5501-6

Published by AA Publishing, a trading name of AA Media Limited, whose registered office is Fanum House, Basing View, Basingstoke, Hampshire RG21 4EA. Registered number 06112600.

Colour separation: Keenes, Andover
Printed and bound in Italy by Printer Trento S.r.l.

Front and back cover images: AA/S L Day

A04460
Maps in this title produced from mapping © MAIRDUMONT / Falk Verlag 2010
Transport map © Communicarta Ltd, UK

About this book

Symbols are used to denote the following categories:

⊞ map reference

✉ address or location

☎ telephone number

🕐 opening times

✋ admission charge

🍴 restaurant or café on premises or nearby

Ⓜ nearest underground train station

🚌 nearest bus/tram route

🚉 nearest overground train station

⛴ nearest ferry stop

ℹ tourist information office

❓ other practical information

↔ other places of interest nearby

► indicates the page where you will find a fuller description

This book is divided into five sections.

Planning pages 6–19
Before You Go; Getting There; Getting Around; Being There

Best places to see pages 20–41
The unmissable highlights of any visit to Barcelona

Exploring pages 42–91
The best places to visit in Barcelona, organized by area

Excursions pages 92–109
Places to visit out of town

Maps pages 113–124
All map references are to the maps at the back of the book. For example, Casa Milà has the reference ⊞ 115 F8 – indicating the page number and grid square in which it is to be found

Contents

PLANNING

6 – 19

BEST PLACES TO SEE

20 – 41

EXPLORING

42 – 91

EXCURSIONS

92 – 109

INDEX & ACKNOWLEDGEMENTS

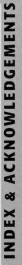

110 – 112

MAPS

113 – 124

Planning

Before You Go   8–11

Getting There   12–13

Getting Around   14–15

Being There   16–19

Before You Go

WHEN TO GO

JAN	FEB	MAR	APR	MAY	JUN	JUL	AUG	SEP	OCT	NOV	DEC
14°C	15°C	17°C	19°C	22°C	25°C	29°C	29°C	27°C	23°C	18°C	15°C
57°F	59°F	62°F	66°F	72°F	77°F	84°F	84°F	80°F	73°F	64°F	59°F

High season Low season

Temperatures are the **average daily maximum** for each month.

The best time to visit Barcelona is May to June or September to October, when the weather is fine but not too hot, and there is a lot going on in the city. July and August see an exodus of locals and many museums, restaurants and shops either close or reduce their opening hours; day-trippers from coastal resorts crowd the city; and the weather can be hot and sticky, with some violent thunderstorms. On the upside, there are plenty of fiestas and festivals to keep you entertained. Winters are cool but seldom cold, though it can snow; when skies are blue and visibility perfect, January and February can be good months of the year.

WHAT YOU NEED

● Required
○ Suggested
▲ Not required

Some countries require a passport to remain valid for a minimum period (usually at least six months) beyond the date of entry – check before you travel.

	UK	Germany	USA	Canada	Australia	Ireland	Netherlands	Spain
Passport (or National Identity Card where applicable)	●	●	●	●	●	●	●	●
Visa (regulations can change – check before you travel)	▲	▲	▲	▲	▲	▲	▲	▲
Onward or Return Ticket	▲	▲	▲	▲	▲	▲	▲	▲
Health Inoculations (tetanus and polio)	▲	▲	▲	▲	▲	▲	▲	▲
Health Documentation (▶ 9, Health Advice)	●	●	●	●	●	●	●	●
Travel Insurance	○	○	○	○	○	○	○	○
Driving Licence (national)	●	●	●	●	●	●	●	●
Car Insurance Certificate	○	○	n/a	n/a	n/a	n/a	○	○
Car Registration Document	●	●	n/a	n/a	n/a	n/a	●	●

ADVANCED PLANNING
Websites
● City Council of Barcelona
www.bcn.es
● Tourist Authority
www.barcelonaturisme.com

TOURIST OFFICES AT HOME
In the UK
Spanish Tourist Office
22–23 Manchester Square
London W1U 3PX
☎ (020) 7486 8077

In the US (New York)
Tourist Office of Spain

666 Fifth Avenue, 35th Floor
New York, NY 10103
☎ (212) 265-8822

In the US (Los Angeles)
Tourist Office of Spain
8383 Wilshire Blvd, Suite 960
Beverly Hills, CA 90211
☎ (323) 658-7195

In Germany
Tourist Office of Spain
Myliusstrasse, 14
60323 Frankfurt Main
☎ (49) 69 72 50 38

HEALTH ADVICE
Insurance
Nationals of EU countries can obtain medical treatment at reduced cost with the relevant documentation (EHIC – European Health Insurance Card), although private medical insurance is still advised and is essential for all other visitors.

Dental services
Dental treatment is not free of charge. A list of *dentistas* can be found in the yellow pages. Dental treatment should be covered by private medical insurance.

TIME DIFFERENCES

GMT	Barcelona	Germany	USA (NY)	Netherlands	Rest of Spain
12 noon	1PM	1PM	7AM	1PM	1PM

Like the rest of Spain, Catalonia is one hour ahead of Greenwich Mean Time (GMT+1), except from late March to late October, when summer time (GMT+2) operates.

WHAT'S ON WHEN

The venues and events listed here are liable to change from one year to the next and in the case of major festivals, there is often more than one venue. Dates also vary slightly from year to year.

January

Reis Mags (5–6 Jan): the Three Kings arrive by boat, then tour the city, showering the crowds with sweets.

February

Santa Eulàlia (12–19 Feb): a series of cultural and musical events in honour of one of the city's patron saints.
Carnestoltes: one week of pre-Lenten carnival celebrations and costumed processions come to an end on Ash Wednesday with the symbolic burial of a sardine.

March

Sant Medir de Gràcia (3 Mar): procession of traditionally dressed horsemen from Gràcia who ride over Collserola to the Hermitage of Sant Medir (Saint of Broad Beans) for a bean-feast.

March/April

Setmana Santa: religious services and celebrations for Easter Week include a solemn procession from the church of Sant Augustì on Good Friday.

April

Sant Jordi (23 Apr); the Catalan alternative to St Valentine's Day.

May

Festa de la Bicicleta (one Sun in May): join the Mayor and 15,000 others on a cycle-ride around the city, to encourage fewer cars.

NATIONAL HOLIDAYS

JAN	FEB	MAR	APR	MAY	JUN	JUL	AUG	SEP	OCT	NOV	DEC
2	0	1(1)	(1)	(1)1	(1)1	0	1	2	1	1	4

1 Jan	New Year's Day
6 Jan	Three King's
19 Mar	Sant Josep
Mar/Apr	Easter
1 May	Labour Day
May/Jun	Whit Sunday
24 Jun	St John
15 Aug	Assumption Day
11 Sep	Catalan National Day
24 Sep	Our Lady of Mercy
12 Oct	Hispanitat
1 Nov	All Saints' Day

6 Dec	Constitution Day
8 Dec	Feast of the Immaculate Conception
25 Dec	Christmas Day
26 Dec	Sant Esteve

Most banks, businesses, museums and shops are closed on these days.

June
Midsummer (23–24 June) is a good excuse for partying and fireworks.
Trobada Castellera (mid-June): displays of human-tower building.
International Film Festival (last two weeks).
Flamenco Festival (last two weeks).
Festival del Grec; arts festival (end Jun–Aug).

July
Aplec de la Sardana, Olot; the biggest *Sardana* dancing festival in Catalonia.

August
Festa Major de Gràcia (3rd week of Aug): a popular festival of music, dancing and street celebrations in the Gràcia district (▶ 73).

September
Diada de Catalunya (11 Sep): Catalonia's National Day does not mark a victory, but the taking of the city by Felipe V in 1714.
La Mercè (20–24 Sep): parades featuring giants, devils, dragons, big heads and fireworks.
Festa Major de la Barceloneta (1–15 Oct): a lively district *feste*, with processions and dancing on the beach every night.

October
International Jazz Festival: this big festival draws international names.

December
Christmas festivities include a craft fair outside the cathedral (6–23 Dec) and a crib in Plaça Sant Jaume.

Getting There

BY AIR

Spain's national airline, Iberia, has scheduled flights to Barcelona's El Prat de Llobregat Airport from major Spanish and European cities. The city is served by over 30 international airlines and has direct flights to more than 80 international destinations. Non-stop flights are operated from New York by Iberia, in association with its partner in the Oneworld alliance, American Airlines. Most flights from North America involve a stop at Madrid or one of the other leading European airports, although Continental and Delta Airlines also fly nonstop to Barcelona from several US airports. There is intense competition from the UK and Ireland – especially from London. The lowest fares are often on the no-frills airlines. These include easyJet, from Gatwick, Luton and Stansted and Ryan Air which flies from London Stansted and Luton to Girona (80km/50 miles north of Barcelona) from where there is a connecting bus to Barcelona. British Airways and its alliance partner, Iberia, fly from Gatwick, Heathrow, Birmingham and Manchester. British Midland (bmi) flies from Heathrow, and easyJet also flies from Liverpool to

Barcelona. Iberia flies from Dublin, in association with its Oneworld partner Aer Lingus. There are no direct flights to Spain from Australia or New Zealand; connections via London, Frankfurt or Paris are the most common. Approximate flying times to Barcelona: London (1.5 hours), Liverpool (2 hours), New York (8 hours).

Ticket prices Flight prices tend to be highest in spring and summer (Easter to September). A good way to solve the problem of finding somewhere to stay, especially at busy times, is to buy a city-break package that includes flights and accommodation. Check with airlines, travel agents, tour-operators and the internet for the current best deals.

It's 12km (14 miles) from El Prat de Llobregat Airport to the city centre and takes 20 to 40 minutes, depending on public transport used.

BY RAIL

The main regional, national and international rail station is Sants-Estació. Comfortable, fast, express trains connect the city to Paris, Madrid and Valencia.

DRIVING

Drive on the right.

Speed limits on motorways (autopistas): **120kph/74mph**
Speed limits on main roads: **100kph/62mph**
Speed limits on minor roads: **90kph/55mph**
In towns (Poblaciones): **50kph/31mph.**

Seat belts must be worn at all times where fitted.

Drink driving Random breath-testing takes place. Never drive under the influence of alcohol.

Fuel (gasolina) is available as: unleaded or sin plomo (90 octane), gasoleo or gasoil (diesel). Super (96 octane) is being phased out. Fuel stations are normally open 6am–10pm, and closed Sundays, though larger ones are open 24 hours. Most take credit cards.

Getting Around

PUBLIC TRANSPORT

Metro The metro is the easiest and fastest way of moving around the city. There are two different underground train systems, the Metro with its six lines identified by number and colour, and the FGC (☎ 93 205 15 15) with two lines in Barcelona and four more lines going to nearby towns.

Buses Barcelona has an excellent bus network; pick up a free plan from any tourist office. Timetables are also shown at individual bus stops. Buses run 6am–10pm. At night there is a *Nitbus* with routes centred on Plaça de Catalunya. Throughout the year the *Bus Turístic*, a hop-on-hop-off service, circuits the main city sights.

Trains The Spanish railway system, RENFE, runs trains from Barcelona to all the major cities in Spain and some outside. Many main-line trains stop at the underground stations at Passeig de Gràcia and Plaça de Catalunya. There are two main railway stations: Estació de Sants and Estació de França near Barceloneta.

Boat The best way to admire the port and coastline is from the sea. *Golondrinas* offer 35-minute harbour tours or 2-hour voyages to the Port Olímpic (➤ 63). Barcelona is the biggest port in the Mediterranean, but the only regular passenger services are to the Balearic islands and to Genoa, Italy.

Cable cars, funiculars and trams

A cable car connects the lower city with Montjuïc castle and links with the funicular railway. The best way to reach Tibidabo is to take the Tramvia Blau (Blue Tram), then the Funicular del Tibidabo to the Amusement Park at the top of the hill.

TAXIS

Pick up a black and yellow taxi at a taxi rank or hail one if it's displaying a green light and the sign *Lliure/Libre* (free). Fares are not unduly expensive but extra fees are charged for airport trips and for baggage. Prices are shown on a sticker inside.

CAR

If you break down in your own car and are a member of a motoring organization with a reciprocal agreement (such as AA or RAC in the UK) contact the Real Automóvil Club de España (RACE) (☎ 902 40 45 45, www.race.es) which has English-speaking staff and offers 24-hour breakdown assistance. Most international rental firms provide a rescue service.

CAR RENTAL

The leading international car rental companies have offices at Barcelona airport and you can book a car in advance (essential in peak periods) either direct or through a travel agent. Local companies offer competitive rates and will usually deliver a car to the airport.

CONCESSIONS

Students Holders of an International Student Identity Card (ISIC) or Euro 26 card might obtain some concessions on travel, entrance fees etc. Most museums offer 50 per cent discount to students, and many are free on the first Sunday of each month. There are several IYHF youth hostels in the city, with accommodation in multi-bed dormitories. Expect to pay around €8–12 per person.

Senior citizens Barcelona is a popular destination for older travellers, especially during winter. Most museums and galleries offer a 50 per cent discount for older people.

Being There

TOURIST OFFICES

The main tourist office is situated beneath Plaça de Catalunya (and is well signposted). It provides a number of services including hotel reservations, currency exchange, walking tours and theatre and concert tickets.

There are branches of the city tourist office on the ground floor of the city hall and at the Sants railway station.

There are also tourist information offices in the airport arrival halls, open daily 9–9.

● Turisme de Barcelona
Plaça de Catalunya 17
www.barcelonaturisme.com
☎ 93 368 97 30
🕐 Daily 9–9

● Plaça Sant Jaume I
🕐 Mon–Sat 10–8, Sun 10–2
Sants Railway Station (Estació de Sants)
🕐 Mon–Fri 8–8, Sat–Sun 8–2

● Turisme de Catalunya
Palau Robert
Passeig de Gràcia 107
www.gencat.net
☎ 93 285 38 34
🕐 Daily 9–9

In summer, information booths can be found at Sagrada Família and La Rambla. In the Barri Gòtic, you may also come across uniformed tourist officials, known as 'Red Jackets'.

EMBASSIES AND CONSULATES
UK ☎ 93 366 62 00
Germany ☎ 93 292 10 00
USA ☎ 93 280 22 27
Netherlands ☎ 93 410 62 10
France ☎ 93 270 30 00

TELEPHONES
Increasingly public phones require a phonecard *(tarjeta)*. You can buy

OPENING HOURS

- Shops
- Offices
- Banks
- Museums/Monuments
- Churches
- Pharmacies

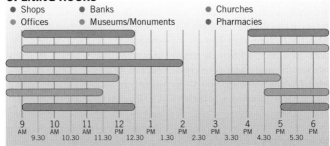

Large department stores and supermarkets may open outside these times, especially during the summer. Banks generally close on Saturdays, although some main branches open in the morning 8.30–12.30. Outside banking hours,

money-exchange facilities are available at the airport and Sants railway station. Some *barris* (districts) also have their own separate feast days, when some shops and offices may close.

these from post offices, news-stands and *estancs* (tobacconists).

Calls from phones in bars and cafés are more expensive than those made from phone booths on the street.

The best place to make international calls is from *locutorios* (phone centres), chiefly found in the Raval district. International cheap rates apply from 8pm to 8am and all weekend.

If you are travelling with your mobile phone, prepaid call time and SIM cards are available, provided you own a GSM, dual or triband cellular phone.

EMERGENCY TELEPHONE NUMBERS
City police (Policía Municipal) 092
National police (Policía nacional) 091
Fire (Bomberos) 080
Ambulance (Ambuláncia) 061

INTERNATIONAL DIALLING CODES
Dial 00 followed by
UK: 44
USA / Canada: 1
Irish Republic: 353
Australia: 61
France: 33
Germany: 49

POSTAL SERVICES

The main *Oficina Central* (post office) at Via Laietana 1 is open Mon–Sat 8.30am–9pm, Sun 8am–2pm, and the Eixample post office at Carrer d'Aragó 282 is open Mon–Fri 8am–9pm and Sat 9–2. You can also buy stamps at any *estanc* (tobacconist).

ELECTRICITY

The power supply is usually 220 volts but a few old buildings are still wired for 125 volts.

Sockets take two-round-pin-style plugs, so an adaptor is needed for most non-Continental appliances and a transformer for appliances operating on 110–120 volts.

CURRENCY AND FOREIGN EXCHANGE

The euro (€) is the official currency of Spain. Banknotes are in denominations of €5, €10, €20, €50, €100, €200 and €500; coins are in denominations of 1, 2, 5, 10, 20 and 50 cents, and €1 and €2.

You can change travellers' cheques at banks and *caixes d'estalvis* (savings banks), at *oficines de canvi* (including late-night bureaux de change along Las Ramblas) and at stations and airports. Bureaux de change don't charge commission but apply (often far) less favourable rates.

Credit cards are widely accepted in shops, restaurants and hotels. Some shops may require proof of identity (no copies). VISA, Mastercard, AMEX and Diners Club are the preferred cards, and they can be used to withdraw cash from widespread ATMs.

HEALTH AND SAFETY
Sun advice

The sunniest (and hottest) months are July and August, with an average of 11 hours sun a day and daytime temperatures of 29°C

TIPS/GRATUITIES

Yes ✓   No ✗

Hotels (if service included)	✓	change
Restaurants (if service not included)	✓	5%
Cafés/bars (if service not included)	✓	change
Taxis	✓	change
Tour guides	✓	€1
Porters	✓	€1
Hairdressers	✓	change
Cloakroom attendants	✓	change
Theatre/cinema usherettes	✓	change
Toilets	✗	

(84°F). Whatever the month you should avoid the midday sun and use a strong sunblock.

Pharmacies

Prescription and non-prescription drugs and medicines are available from *farmàcias* (pharmacies), distinguished by a large green cross. They are able to dispense many drugs that would be available only on prescription in some other countries.

Safe water

Tap water is generally safe though it can be heavily chlorinated. Mineral water is cheap to buy and is sold as *con gaz* (carbonated) and *sin gaz* (still). Drink plenty of water during hot weather.

Police

The Policía Municipal (navy-blue uniforms) keep law and order in the city. For a police station ask for *la comisaría*. To help prevent crime:

- Do not carry more cash than you need.
- Beware of pickpockets in markets, tourist sights or crowded places.
- Avoid walking alone in dark alleys at night, especially in the Barri Xines.
- Leave valuables and important documents the safe.

CLOTHING SIZES

France	UK	Rest of Europe	USA	
46	36	46	36	
48	38	48	38	
50	40	50	40	
52	42	52	42	
54	44	54	44	Suits
56	46	56	46	
41	7	41	8	
42	7.5	42	8.5	
43	8.5	43	9.5	
44	9.5	44	10.5	
45	10.5	45	11.5	Shoes
46	11	46	12	
37	14.5	37	14.5	
38	15	38	15	
39/40	15.5	39/40	15.5	
41	16	41	16	
42	16.5	42	16.5	Shirts
43	17	43	17	
36	8	34	6	
38	10	36	8	
40	12	38	10	
42	14	40	12	
44	16	42	14	Dresses
46	18	44	16	
38	4.5	38	6	
38	5	38	6.5	
39	5.5	39	7	
39	6	39	7.5	
40	6.5	40	8	Shoes
41	7	41	8.5	

Best places to see

Casa Milà 22–23

Catedral 24–25

Fundació Joan Miró 26–27

Montjuïc 28–29

Museu Nacional d'Art de Catalunya
(MNAC) 30–31

Museu Picasso 32–33

Parc Güell 34–35

Las Ramblas 36–37

La Sagrada Família 38–39

Santa Maria del Mar 40–41

1 Casa Milà

This apartment block is Antoni Gaudí's last and most famous secular building. Its roof terrace is an iconic image of the city.

Built between 1906 and 1912, Casa Milà shows this great Catalan architect at his most inventive. It also shows Gaudí's genius as a structural engineer, with seven storeys built entirely on columns and arches, supposedly without a single straight line or right-angled corner. Its most distinctive features are the rippling limestone façade, with its intricate ironwork, and the strangely shaped chimneys of the roof terrace. In fact, the large amount of limestone is what gave rise to the building's nickname of La Pedrera (the quarry).

After years of neglect, Casa Milà was declared a World Heritage Site by UNESCO in 1984, and purchased by the Caixa Catalunya Foundation, which invested over 8,000 million pesetas to restore it to its original glory.

✚ 115 F8 ✉ Carrer Provença 261–265 ☎ 93 484 59 00 🕐 Daily 10–7.30. Guided tours: Mon–Fri at 5.30 in English and Catalan and at 6.30 in Spanish 🎫 Expensive 🚇 Diagonal ❓ Audio-guide available

2 Catedral

Barcelona's great cathedral is not only one of the most celebrated examples of Catalan Gothic style, but also one of the finest cathedrals in Spain.

The cathedral is located at the heart of the Barri Gòtic (➤ 46–48), on the remains of an early Christian basilica and a Romanesque church. Most of the building was erected between the late 13th century and the middle of the 15th century, although the heavily ornate main façade and octagonal dome were constructed at the beginning of the 20th century.

The impressive interior represents a harmonious blend of medieval and Renaissance styles, with a lofty triple nave, graceful arches, 29 side chapels and an intricately carved choir. Beneath the main altar is the crypt of Santa Eulàlia (the patron saint of Barcelona), which contains her tomb.

Near the main entrance is the Chapel of Christ of Lepanto (formerly the Chapter House), which is widely considered to be the finest example of

Gothic art in the cathedral. It contains the crucifix carried on board *La Real*, the flagship of Don Juan of Austria, during the famous Battle of Lepanto. The 14th-century cloister is the most beautiful part of the cathedral, its garden of magnolias, palms and fountains making a cool retreat from the heat of Barcelona. There is even a small pond, with a flock of white geese, supposedly symbolizing Santa Eulàlia's virginal purity. A small museum just off the cloister shelters many of the cathedral's most precious treasures.

Despite its grandeur, the cathedral remains very much a people's church. The main entrance is at the Plaça de la Seu and there is a side entrance along the Carrer del Bisbe that leads to the cloister. Worshippers outnumber tourists and on Sundays Barcelonans gather in Plaça de la Seu at noon to perform the *sardana*, Catalonia's stately national dance which symbolizes unity.

✚ 122 C3 ✉ Plaça de la Seu 3 ☎ 93 315 15 54 🕐 Daily 8–1.15, 5–7.30 🖐 Free 🚇 Jaume I 🚌 17, 19, 40, 45
Museum
🕐 Daily 10–12.45, 5–6.45 🖐 Inexpensive
❓ Small gift shop

3 Fundació Joan Miró

www.bcn.fjmiro.es

This dazzling gallery pays homage to Joan Miró, one of Catalonia's greatest artists, famous for his childlike style and use of vibrant colours.

The Miró Foundation was set up by Joan Miró in 1971, and is devoted to the study of his works and to the promotion of all contemporary art. The gallery – a modern building of white spaces, massive windows and skylights designed by Josep Lluís Sert – is itself a masterpiece and a perfect place in which to pursue the Foundation's aims. It contains some 300 Mirónian paintings, 150 sculptures, nine tapestries, his complete graphic works and over 8,000 drawings, making it one of the world's most complete collections of this great master.

Miró was born in Barcelona in 1893 and, apart from a brief spell in Paris, spent most of his life in the city developing his bold style of vigorous lines and intense primary colours. In 1956 he moved to Mallorca, and remained on the island until his death in 1983.

Highlights of the gallery include some of Miró's earliest sketches, the tapestry *Tapis de la Fundació* and a set of black-and-white lithographs entitled *Barcelona Series* (1939–44) – an artistic appraisal of the war years. The roof terrace and gardens contain several striking sculptures.

The Foundation also presents temporary exhibitions of modern art, contemporary music recitals and a special permanent collection called

'To Joan Miró', with works by Ernst, Tàpies, Calder and Matisse among others, a touching tribute to the person and his work.

🕇 118 D4 ✉ Avinguda de Miramar, Montjuïc ☎ 93 443 94 70 🕐 Oct–Jun Tue–Sat 10–7, Thu 10–9.30, Sun 10–2.30; Jul–Sep Tue–Sat 10–8, Thu 10–9.30, Sun 10–2.30 ✋ Expensive 🍴 Café (€€) Ⓜ Espanya 🚌 50, 55

4 Montjuïc

Few can resist the charms of the city's local hill, with its museums, galleries, gardens and other attractions set in an oasis of natural calm.

Montjuïc, 213m (700ft) high, is south of the city and the dominant feature of its coast and skyline. It's history has been linked to the city's history since prehistoric times. The Romans later called it 'Jove's Mountain' but today it is called 'Mountain of the Jews', after an early Jewish necropolis here. The castle, standing on the bluff, dates from the 16th to 18th centuries and houses the **Museu Militar**, exhibiting collections of military weaponry and uniforms from different countries and periods.

In 1929 Montjuïc was the venue for the International Expo. Today many of its buildings are filled with museums. The **Museu Arqueològic** and the **Museu Etnològic** typify the Expo's architecture, as does the Palau Nacional, home of the Museu Nacional d'Art de Catalunya (➤ 30–31).

Beneath the Palau Nacional, Plaça d'Espanya marks the main entrance to the Expo with Venetian towers, and an avenue leading to Plaça de la Font Màgica – 'Magic Fountain' – a spectacular sight that always draws the crowds. The road continues up past the Pavelló Mies van der Rohe (➤ 85) and the Poble Espanyol (➤ 86) to Fundació Joan Miró (➤ 26–27) and L'Anella Olímpica (➤ 82–83), venue for much of the 1992 Olympic Games.

🚇 118 D4 🚶 Free 🍴 Cafés and restaurants (€–€€)
🚇 Espanya 🚌 50, 51 🚠 Montjuïc funicular from Paral.lel
Museums
☎ Museu Militar: 93 329 86 13. Museu Arqueològic: 93 424 65 77. Museu Etnològic: 93 424 68 07 🕐 Tue–Sun, times vary 🚶 Inexpensive

5 Museu Nacional d'Art de Catalunya (MNAC)

www.mnac.es

Dominating the northern flank of Montjuïc, this imposing neoclassical palace contains a treasure trove of Catalan art spanning several centuries.

The National Museum of Catalan Art is one of the best museums of medieval and Catalan art in the world. Housed in the extravagant National Exhibition building, built as the symbol of the 1929 World Exhibition (➤ 86), the museum boasts the world's most eminent Romanesque art collection. This includes stone sculptures, wood carvings, gold and silverwork, altar cloths, enamels and coins and a beautifully presented series of 11th- and 12th-century murals, carefully stripped from church walls throughout Catalonia and precisely reconstructed in apses, as if they were still in their original locations.

The idea for this collection originated in the early 20th century when the theft of national architectural treasures in Catalonia was at its height, instigating a church-led crusade to move

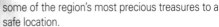

some of the region's most precious treasures to a safe location.

The museum's Gothic collection forms a striking contrast with over 400 highly ornate retables and sculptures, including an extraordinary 15th-century Virgin in full flamenco dress. A somewhat fragmented collection of Renaissance and baroque paintings embraces works by Tintoretto, El Greco and Zurbarán.

The modern art collection is devoted to Catalan art from the mid-19th century to around 1930. The collection starts with works by Maria Fortuny, the earliest of the *Modernistas* and the first Catalan artist to be known widely abroad, and friends Ramon Casas, whose work once hung on the walls of Els Quatre Gats, and Santiago Rusinyol. However, the highlight is the decorative arts collection: jewellery, textiles, stained glass and ironwork.

The building also contains the Museum of Drawings and Prints, the Numismatic Museum of Catalonia, and will eventually house the General Library of Art History.

✚ 118 C3 ✉ Palau Nacional, Parc de Montjuïc ☎ 93 622 03 76 🕒 Tue–Sat 10–7, Sun and public hols 10–2.30 ♿ Expensive; free first Thu of month 🍴 Café-bar (€) 🚇 Espanya 🚌 9, 13, 30, 50, 55

6 Museu Picasso

www.museupicasso.bcn.es

This fascinating museum traces the career of the most acclaimed artist of modern times, from early childhood sketches to the major works of later years.

The Picasso Museum is the city's biggest tourist attraction. It contains one of the world's most important collections of Picasso's work and until 2003, when the impressive Museo Picasso Málaga opened in his birthplace, was the only one of significance in his native country.

Pablo Ruiz Picasso was born in Andaluciá, but moved to the Catalan capital in 1895, aged 14. He was an exceptionally gifted artist and, by the time of his first exhibition in 1900, was well known. In 1904 he moved to Paris, but remained in contact with Barcelona.

The museum contains work from his early years, notably a series of impressionistic landscapes and seascapes, a portrait of his aunt, *Tía Pepa* (1896), notebook sketches and paintings of street scenes, including *Sortida del Teatre* (1896) and La *Barceloneta* (1897), and the menu for *Els Quatre Gats* (Four Cats) café. Other works are from the Blue Period (1901–04), the Pink Period

(1904–06), the Cubist (1907–20) and Neo-classical (1920–25) periods, through to the mature works of later years. There are also 41 ceramic pieces donated in 1982 by his wife, Jacqueline which graphically demonstrate Picasso's astonishing artistic development.

✚ 121 D5 ✉ Carrer Montcada 15–23 ☎ 93 319 63 10 🕒 Tue–Sat 10–8, Sun 10–3 ✋ Expensive; free first Sun of month 🍴 Café-restaurant (€€) Ⓜ Jaume I 🚌 14, 17, 19, 36, 39, 40, 45, 51, 57, 59, 64, 157

7 Parc Güell

Deemed a failure in its day, Gaudí's eccentric hilltop park is now considered one of the city's treasures and a unique piece of landscape design.

The architectural work of Gaudí is inseparable from Barcelona, largely thanks to his relationship with the Güells, a family of industrialists who commissioned from him a number of works. For Parc Güell, Don Eusebi Güell, Gaudí's main patron,

had grand ideas for a residential English-style garden city, with 60 houses set in formal gardens. Gaudí worked on the project from 1900 to 1914, but it proved an economic disaster: only three houses were completed, and the park became city property in 1923.

The park's main entrance is marked by two eccentric pavilions. A grand stairway, ornamented by a dragon fountain, leads to a massive cavernous space, originally intended as the marketplace. Its forest of pillars supports a rooftop plaza bordered by a row of curved benches, covered in multicoloured *trencadís* (broken ceramics).

Throughout the 20ha (50 acres) of Mediterranean parkland, there are sculptures, steps and paths raised on columns of 'dripping' stonework. Gaudí himself lived in one of the houses from 1906 to 1926. Built by his pupil Berenguer, it is now the Casa-Museu Gaudí and contains models, furniture, drawings and other memorabilia of the architect and his colleagues.

✚ 117 C5 ✉ Main entrance: Carrer Olot ☎ 93 413 24 00 🕐 May–Aug daily 10–9; Sep, Apr daily 10–8; Oct, Mar daily 10–7; Nov–Feb daily 10–6 💷 Free 🍴 Self-service bar 🚇 Lesseps or Vallcarca (and uphill walk) 🚌 24, 25, 28, 87

8 Las Ramblas

Sooner or later, every visitor joins the locals swarming day and night down Las Ramblas, one of the most famous walkways in Spain.

The name Las Ramblas, derived from *ramla* (Arabic for 'torrent'), serves as a reminder that in earlier times, the street was a sandy gully that ran parallel to the medieval wall, and carried rainwater down to the sea. Today's magnificent 18th-century tree-lined walkway, running through the heart of the old city down to the port, is the pride of Barcelona. The central promenade is split into various distinctive sections strung head-to-tail, each with their own history and characteristics, from the flower stalls along Rambla de les Flors to the birdcages of Rambla dels Ocells. And it is said if you drink from the famous fountain in La Rambla de Canaletes you are sure to return to the city. The other parts of Las Ramblas are La Rambla dels Estudis, named after the university that was once here, La Rambla dels Caputxins, the section that's home to the

famous Liceu theatre, and La Rambla de Santa Mònica, the stretch nearest to the port.

Promenading Las Ramblas is never the same twice, changing with the seasons, by the day and by the hour. It's an experience eagerly shared by people from every walk of life – tourists, locals, bankers, Barça football fans, artists, beggars, street-performers, newspaper-sellers, pickpockets, nightclubbers, students, lovers and theatre crowds – all blending together with the noise of the traffic, the birdsong, the buskers (street musicians) and the scent of the flowers. Such is the significance to the city of this promenade *par excellence*, that two words – *ramblejar* (a verb meaning 'to walk down the Rambla') and *ramblista* (an adjective describing someone addicted to the act of *ramblejar*) – have been adopted in its honour.

🚉 122 E1–B2 🍴 Plenty (€–€€€) 🚇 Catalunya, Drassanes, Liceu 🚌 14, 38, 59, 91 ❓ Beware of pickpockets that may be in the area

9 La Sagrada Família

www.sagradafamilia.org

Big Ben, the Eiffel Tower...most cities have a distinctive monument. Barcelona has Gaudí's Sagrada Família, his, as yet unfinished, cathedral.

Antoni Gaudí, the internationally prestigious figure of Catalan architecture, started work on La Sagrada Família (Temple of the Holy Family) in 1882, and for the latter part of his life dedicated himself entirely to his great vision for Europe's biggest cathedral.

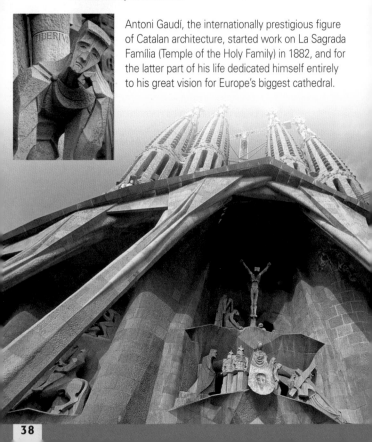

His dream was to include three façades representing the birth, death and resurrection of Christ, and eighteen mosaic-clad towers symbolizing the Twelve Apostles, the four Evangelists, the Virgin Mary and Christ. On his untimely death in 1926 (he was run over by a tram on the Gran Via), only the crypt, one of the towers, the majority of the east (Nativity) façade and the apse were completed. Ever since, the fate of the building has been the subject of often bitter debate.

With a further estimated 80 years of work (which would include the destruction of several buildings in Carrer Mallorca and Carrer Valencia), it seems that the Sagrada Família will probably never be more than a shell. Even as it stands today, it has become a world-wide symbol of Barcelona, one of the great architectural wonders of the world, and a must on every visitor's itinerary. A video about the history and construction of La Sagrada Família is included in the entrance price.

➕ 121 A7 ✉ Plaça Sagrada Família ☎ 93 207 30 31
🕐 Apr–Sep daily 9–8; Oct–Mar daily 9–6 💵 Expensive; additional charge for lift 🚇 Sagrada Família 🚌 19, 33, 34, 43, 44, 50, 51, 54 ❓ Crypt museum, gift shop, lift and stairway to the towers

10 Santa Maria del Mar

This beautiful Gothic triumph was built to demonstrate Catalan supremacy in Mediterranean commerce.

The 14th-century church of Santa Maria del Mar (St Mary of the Sea) is at the heart of La Ribera (The Waterfront), the medieval city's maritime and trading district. This neighbourhood's link with the sea dates back to the 10th century, when a settlement grew up here along the seashore outside the city walls, around a chapel called Santa Maria de les Arenes (St Mary of the Sands). During the 13th century, the settlement grew and became known as Vilanova de Mar. Its identity was eventually firmly established with the transformation of the tiny chapel into the magnificent church of Santa Maria del Mar, built on what was then the seashore, as a show of maritime wealth and power. Indeed, the foundation stone commemorated the Catalan conquest of Sardinia.

The church was built between 1329 and 1384 and has a purity of style that makes it one of the finest examples of Barcelona's Gothic heritage. The plain exterior is characterized by predominantly horizontal lines and two octagonal, flat-roofed towers. Inside, the wide, soaring nave and high, narrow aisles, all supported by slim, octagonal

columns, provide a great sense of spaciousness. Sadly, the ornaments of the side chapels were lost when the city was besieged, once by Bourbon troops in 1714 and again during the Spanish Civil War. The resulting bareness of the interior, apart from the sculpture of a 15th-century ship that sits atop the altar, enables you to admire the church's striking simplicity without distraction.

✚ 121 D5 ✉ Plaça de Santa Maria
☎ 93 310 23 90 🕐 Mon–Sat 9–1.30,
4.30–8, Sun 10–1.30, 4.30–8 ✋ Free
Ⓜ Barceloneta, Jaume I 🚌 14, 17, 36, 39,
40, 45, 51, 57, 59, 64, 157

Exploring

Las Ramblas and around	45–60
La Ribera to Port Olímpic	61–68
The Eixample and Gràcia	69–80
Montjuïc to Sants	81–86
Pedralbes and Tibidabo	87–91

Ever since it was founded over 2,000 years ago, Barcelona has been striving to become a great metropolis. To its inhabitants, it is not Spain's second city but the capital of Catalonia; not a Spanish metropolis but a European one, and the Spanish leader in both *haute couture* and *haute cuisine*. The best time to see Barcelona in its true colours is after FC Barça wins an important match, and the streets erupt to the sound of car horns and popping champagne corks.

Visitors to Barcelona, on the other hand, are entranced by the Mediterranean atmosphere of the city, the richness of its art and architectural treasures both ancient and modern, the proud but not narrowly nationalistic character of the people, the strong tradition of theatre and music and the exuberant nightlife. In this dynamic and passionate city, it is easy to live life to the full, both day and night.

Las Ramblas and around

Las Ramblas, one long tree-lined thoroughfare divided into five distinct sections, stretches from Plaça de Catalunya, Barcelona's main square, towards the waterfront. It is the place to sit, to watch street entertainers and, in time, be drawn into the ceaseless flow of pedestrians.

To the left of Las Ramblas is the Barri Gòtic (Gothic Quarter), a maze of dark narrow streets around the cathedral, medieval palaces and churches. Beyond is Port Vell (Old Port), the colourful harbourside, with a marvellous state-of-the-art aquarium, and the Maremagnum, a huge covered entertainment and shopping complex. Antoni Gaudí's magnificent palace, Palau Güell, off the end of the Ramblas in the direction of the port, is set in the lower side of El Raval – a run-down mix of medieval streets, gloomy alleyways and dead-ends. By contrast, the upper part of El Raval is now dominated by the Museu d'Art Contemporàni (MACBA), Barcelona's contemporary art museum set amid stylish restaurants and art galleries galore.

BARRI GÒTIC

The tightly packed maze of narrow streets and alleyways of Barcelona's Ciutat Vella (Old City), bordered by Las Ramblas, the Ciutadella Park, Plaça Catalunya and the sea, was once enclosed by medieval city walls and, until the massive building boom of the Eixample (➤ 70–71), 150 years ago, comprised the entire city.

At its heart is the Barri Gòtic (Gothic Quarter), one of several clearly identifiable *barris* or districts which make up the Old City. Its roots can be traced back to 15 BC, when Roman soldiers established a small settlement called Barcino on a slight hill here called Mons Taber. This remarkable cluster of dark, twisting streets, quiet patios, sun-splashed squares and grand Gothic buildings was built inside the Roman fortifications at a time when Barcelona, along with Genoa and Venice, was one of the three most important merchant cities in the Mediterranean and possessed untold riches. Its crowning glory, the Catedral (➤ 24–25), is surrounded by former residences of the counts of Barcelona and the Kings of Catalonia and Aragón. To the northwest lies Carrer Portaferrissa, the principal shopping street, with sophisticated boutiques and shopping arcades. To the south lies the spacious Plaça Sant Jaume (➤ 59) and a cobweb of narrow streets and interconnecting squares, including Plaça Sant Felip Neri, with its fine baroque church, Plaça del Pi, with its market of local produce, and leafy Plaça Sant Josep Oriol, the 'Montmartre of Barcelona', where local artists display their works at weekends and buskers entertain the café

crowds. Just off the square, the narrow streets bounded by Carrer Banys Nous, Call and Bisbe once housed a rich Jewish ghetto called *El Call*, but now the area is better known for its antiques shops.

As the city grew more prosperous in the early Middle Ages, new *barris* developed around the Roman perimeter, including La Mercè to the south and La Ribera to the east. The area south of Carrer de Ferran – La Mercè – is focused around the elegant, arcaded Plaça Reial (➤ 58) and the Church of La Mercè, Barcelona's patron Virgin. Though once very prosperous, this *barri* has become shabby and run-down, but is still worth exploring if only to seek out the excellent locals' *tapas* bars along Carrer de la Mercè.

✚ 122 C2

CATEDRAL

See pages 24–25.

DRASSANES AND MUSEU MARÍTIM

The Museu Marítim (Maritime Museum) is in the magnificent Drassanes Reials (Royal Shipyards), a splendid example of Gothic civil architecture. Since the 13th century, these yards have been dedicated to the construction of ships for the Crowns of Catalonia and Aragon.

Today, their vast cathedral-like, stone-vaulted halls contain maps, charts, paintings, pleasure craft and a huge range of other seafaring memorabilia chronicling the remarkable maritime history of Barcelona. The most impressive exhibit is a 60m (66yds) replica of *La Real*, flagship of Don Juan of Austria, which forms part of an exciting 45-minute spectacle – 'The Great Sea Adventure'. Through headphones, visual and acoustic effects, visitors can experience life as a galley slave, encounter a Caribbean storm, join emigrants bound for the New World, and explore the seabed on board *Ictineo*, claimed to be the world's first submarine and built by Catalan inventor Narcís Monturiol.

www.diba.es/mmaritim

➕ 119 E7 ✉ Avinguda de les Drassanes s/n ☎ 93 342 99 29 🕐 Daily 10–8
✋ Expensive; free first Sat of each month after 3pm 🍴 Café-restaurant (€)
🚇 Drassanes 🚌 14, 18, 36, 38, 57, 59, 64, 91 ❓ Library, bookshop, gift shop

MERCAT DE LA BOQUERIA

Of more than 40 food markets in Barcelona, La Boqueria is the best and the busiest – always bustling with local shoppers, restaurateurs, gourmands and tourists. Its cavernous market hall (best entered through an imposing wrought-iron entranceway halfway up Las Ramblas) was built in the 1830s to house the food stalls that cluttered Las Ramblas and surrounding streets.

Inside is a riot of noise, perfumes and colours, with a myriad stalls offering all the specialities of the Mediterranean and the Catalonian hinterland – mouth-watering displays of fruit and vegetables, a glistening array of exotic fish, endless strings of sausages, haunches of ham and sweetly scented bunches of herbs.

✚ 122 B1 ✉ Rambla 91 ☎ 93 318 25 84
🕐 Mon–Sat 8am–8pm. Closed public hols
✋ Free 🍴 Snack bars (€) 🚇 Liceu

MONUMENT A COLOM

This vast monument, commemorating the return of Christopher Columbus to Barcelona in 1493 from his first trip to the Americas, stands outside the naval headquarters of Catalonia, at the seaward end of the Ramblas. It was designed by Gaietà Buigas for the Universal Exposition of 1888, with Columbus standing at the top of a column 50m (164ft) high, pointing out to sea – towards Italy! Take the lift to the top for breathtaking bird's-eye views of the harbourfront.

✚ 119 E7 ✉ Plaça Portal de la Pau ☎ 93 302 52 24 🕐 Jun–Sep daily 9–8.30; Oct–May 10–6.30. Closed public hols 👤 Inexpensive Ⓜ Drassanes

MUSEU D'ART CONTEMPORANI DE BARCELONA (MACBA)

The Barcelona Museum of Contemporary Art (MACBA), which celebrated its 10th anniversary in 2005, focuses on the art movements of the second half of the 20th century.

The building, itself a work of art, was designed by the American architect Richard Meier. It has been the subject of much controversy but is increasingly being included as one of Barcelona's must-see landmarks. The vast white edifice with swooping ramps and glass-walled galleries almost upstages the works on display. Its location – surrounded by shabby old houses in the once rundown district of Raval – has spearheaded investment in the neighbourhood.

MACBA's extensive collection (exhibited in rotation) covers the 1940s to the 1990s, with special emphasis on Catalan and Spanish artists. It contains works by Klee, Miró and Tàpies, along with many others, including Joan Brossa, Maurizio Cattelan and Damien Hirst.

🕂 119 C7 ✉ Plaça dels Àngels 1 ☎ 93 412 08 10 🕐 Mon–Fri 11–7.30,
Sat 10–8, Sun and public hols 10–3. Longer opening hours in summer.
Guided tours Wed, Sat 6pm, Sun and public hols noon ✋ Expensive
🍴 Café (€) Ⓜ Catalunya, Universitat

MUSEU FREDERIC MARÈS

This museum was founded by local artist Frederic Marès, probably Spain's most prolific and varied sculptor, in 1946. The entrance is via a beautiful medieval courtyard, which was once part of the Royal Palace of the Kings and Queens of Catalonia and Aragon. The museum itself is divided into two main sections: the sculpture collection, featuring works from the pre-Roman period to the 20th century, and the 'Sentimental Museum', which portrays daily life from the 15th to 20th centuries through an astonishing assortment of household items.

Highlights include the women's section (with collections of fans, parasols, jewellery and hat pins), the smoker's room, and the charming entertainments room, with its puppet theatres, wind-up toys and dolls.

www.museumares.bcn.es

🕂 122 C4 ✉ Plaça de Sant Iu 5–6 ☎ 93 310 58 00
🕐 Tue–Sat 10–7, Sun 10–3 ✋ Moderate; free 1st Sun of month and every Wed pm 🍴 Summer café (€) Ⓜ Jaume I
❓ Library, shop, guided visits

MUSEU D'HISTÒRIA DE LA CIUTAT

The Museu d'Història de la Ciutat (City History Museum) is responsible for researching, conserving and publicizing Barcelona's heritage. It is split into several sections in various locations around the Plaça del Rei (➤ 57). To start, visitors can familiarize themselves with the earliest origins of the city by wandering around the underground walkways beneath the square, which explore a vast area of excavations that have exposed the ancient Roman settlement of Barcino.

The main entrance to the museum complex is at the opposite end of the square, in Casa Padellàs, a medieval mansion which was moved here stone by stone when the Via Laietana was created in 1930. Inside, carefully chosen, thoroughly documented exhibits trace Barcelona's remarkable evolution through two thousand years of history from a Roman trading-post to a wealthy 18th-century metropolis. Climb to the lookout point high above the galleries for memorable views of the square and the old city.

www.museuhistoria.bcn.es

✚ 122 C4 ✉ Plaça del Rei s/n ☎ 93 315 11 11 🕐 Jul–Sep Tue–Sat 10–8, Sun 10–2; Oct–Jun Tue–Sat 10–2, 4–8, Sun 10–2 💷 Moderate; free 1st Sat afternoon of the month 🚇 Jaume I, Liceu ❓ Guided tours

PALAU GÜELL

This extraordinary building, constructed between 1886 and 1888 and declared a World Cultural Heritage site by UNESCO, was Antoni Gaudí's first major architectural project, commissioned by the Güell family.

The façade is particularly striking, with its twin arches leading into the central vestibule. Off the latter are various rooms decorated with *Modernista* fittings. A ramp leads down to the basement stables, constructed with bare-brick columns and arches. The rooftop terrace is a wonderful mixture of random spires, battlements and chimneys of differing shapes and sizes, decorated with coloured ceramic mosaics. Look closely and on one you will find a reproduction of Cobi, the 1992 Barcelona Olympics mascot. Unfortunately, the Güell family did not live here long. In 1936, the palace was confiscated by Spanish Civil War anarchists, who used it as their military headquarters and prison. It is currently closed for renovation.

✚ 122 D1 ✉ Carrer Nou de la Rambla 3–5 ☎ 93 317 39 74 Ⓜ Liceu

PLAÇA DE CATALUNYA

The Plaça de Catalunya is the heart of Barcelona and the hub of the city's transport system. It was first landscaped at the end of the 19th century and became of major importance as the pivotal point between the old and new city: the Barri Gòtic (▶ 46–48) to the east, the Eixample district (▶ 70–71) to the north and west, and, to the southeast, Las Ramblas (▶ 36–37) running down to the port.

Its main landmarks today are the head office of Banco Espanol de Crédito, former headquarters of the unified Socialist Party of Catalonia during the Civil War; the El Corte Inglés department store and a medley of fountains and statues, including work by important sculptors such as Gargallo, Marès and Subirachs. Today, its benches, trees and splashing fountains make it a popular place to meet friends and have a coffee.

✚ 119 C8 ▮▮ Several (€–€€) 🔁 Catalunya

PLAÇA DEL REI

The charming King's Square was once a bustling medieval marketplace. Today, it forms a frequent backdrop to summer open-air concerts and theatrical events, especially during the Grec festival (▶ 11), and is the location not only of the City History Museum (▶ 54) but also of the **Palau Reial Major** (Great Royal Palace), former residence of the Counts of Barcelona.

It was on the steps leading up to the Palau Reial Major that King Ferdinand and Queen Isabella are said to have received Columbus on his return from his first voyage to America in 1493. Inside, the Spanish Inquisition once sat in the Saló del Tinell, exploiting the local myth that should any prisoner lie, the stones on the ceiling would move. Today, the hall functions as an exhibition area.

On the north side of the square is the chapel of Santa Agata (also part of the royal palace), which contains a precious 15th-century altarpiece by Jaume Huguet. On the opposite side of the square, the Palau de Lloctinent (Palace of the Deputy) was built in 1549 for the Catalan representative of the king in Madrid. The strenuous climb to the top of its five-storey lookout tower (the Mirador del Rei Martí) is well rewarded by sweeping views of the old town.

➕ 122 C4 🚇 Jaume I

Palau Reial Major

☎ 93 315 11 11 ⏱ Palace and tower: Tue–Sat 10–2, 4–8, Sun and public hols 10–3 💰 Moderate ❓ Part of the Museu d'Història de la Ciutat (▶ 54)

PLAÇA REIAL

This sunny porticoed square, just off Las Ramblas, with its tall palm trees, decorative fountain and buskers was constructed in 1848. Some of the façades are decorated with terracotta reliefs of navigators and the discoverers of America, and the two tree-like central lampposts mark Gaudí's first commission in Barcelona. The pretty central fountain was inspired by the *Three Graces*.

The myriad bars that line the spacious square are popular with both locals and visitors alike, especially on summer evenings. It is advisable to keep a close watch on your belongings here – the square has a reputation for shady characters and pickpockets, hence the discreet but constant police presence. On Sunday mornings a coin and stamp market is held here.

✚ 122 D2 🍴 Plenty (€–€€) 🚇 Liceu, Drassanes

PLAÇA SANT JAUME

Once the hub of Roman Barcelona, this impressive square today represents the city's political heart, and is dominated by two buildings; the neoclassical and Gothic **Casa de la Ciutat** (Town Hall) and, directly opposite, the Renaissance **Palau de la Generalitat de Catalunya** (Government of Catalonia).

The origins of Barcelona's municipal authority date back to 1249, when Jaume I granted the city the right to elect councillors, giving rise to the creation of the Consell de Cent (Council of One Hundred). The famous Saló de Cent (Chamber of One Hundred) and the black marble Saló de las Cronicas (Chamber of the Chronicles) are among the architectural highlights of the Town Hall.

✚ 122 D3 🍴 Cafés (€) 🚇 Jaume I

Casa de la Ciutat/Ajuntament

☎ 93 402 70 00 🕙 Sun 10–1.30 ✋ Free

Palau de la Generalitat de Catalunya

☎ 93 402 46 00 🕙 Guided tours every 30 mins, 10.30–1.30 every 2nd and 4th Sun of each month ✋ Free

PORT VELL

Although Barcelona was founded on sea-going tradition, for many years its seafront was in decay, until a major redevelopment prior to the 1992 Olympics reintegrated the Port Vell (Old Port) into the city by transforming it into a lively entertainment venue. The Rambla de Mar, a series of undulating wooden walkways and bridges, acts as an extension of Las Ramblas, connecting the city to Port Vell's many attractions.

Maremagnum, Port Vell's biggest crowd puller, is a covered shopping and entertainment centre with smart boutiques, restaurants, trendy bars, discos and fast-food joints. Adjacent to the conventional cinema complex, IMAX shows films in 3D, with state-of-the-art wrap-around screens and sound. Near by is the Aquarium, one of the biggest and best in Europe.

Take a *Golondrina* for the afternoon for a different perspective of the harbour developments. The luxurious marina, with more than 400 berths, is one of the Mediterranean's most exclusive anchorages.

 119 E7 🖐 Free 🍴 Cafés, bars and restaurants (€–€€€) 🚇 Drassanes, Barceloneta

Golondrinas

✉ Moll de les Drassanes ☎ 93 442 31 06 🕐 Times of boat trips vary according to season 🖐 Moderate 🚇 Drassanes

LAS RAMBLAS

See pages 36–37.

La Ribera to Port Olímpic

La Ribera, one of the oldest districts of Barcelona, has become home to buzzing *tapas* bars, wine bars and stylish restaurants situated in Gothic palaces and Manhattan-style factory conversions.

The northern half of the district, Sant Pere, contains the Modernist masterpiece Palau de la Música Catalana. Carrer de Montcada, in the Born, is now a showcase of art galleries and museums, including the Museu Picasso, one of the city's biggest attractions. The lanes around Carrer de Montcada are full of

workshops where jewellers and potters carry on their trade much as they did in medieval times.

Passeig del Born, the main thoroughfare through the Born, is a lively promenade lined with jazz clubs and cocktail bars. Here you'll find the Basílica de Santa Maria del Mar, known as the fishermen's cathedral. A pleasant waterfront walk leads from La Ribera around the fishing village of Barceloneta to the popular beaches on either side of Port Olímpic.

LA BARCELONETA AND PORT OLÍMPIC

Following the siege and conquest of Barcelona by Felipe V in 1714, a large area of the Ribera district was destroyed to make way for a new citadel. The displaced residents lived for years in makeshift shelters on the beach, until in 1755 a new district was developed on a triangular wedge of reclaimed land between the harbour and the sea, named La Barceloneta (Little Barcelona).

In the 19th century, La Barceloneta became home to seamen and dockers and it is still a working district, retaining its shantytown atmosphere, fishy smells and a quayside lined with the boats. Today visitors come here to eat in the fine seafood eateries (*chiringuitos*), in particular those along the main harbourside thoroughfare, Passeig Joan de Borbó, and the restaurants of the converted Palau de Mar warehouse (▶ 64–65).

By contrast, Port Olímpic, with its smart promenades and glittering marina, has given new impetus to Barcelona's nautical activities. Its chic restaurants, cafés and bars have become a lively night spot popular with both locals and tourists alike. Spain's two tallest buildings preside over the port – the office-filled Torre Mapfre and the five-star hotel Arts Barcelona, Barcelona's top hotel. Near by, a striking bronze fish sculpture by Frank Gehry (architect of the Guggenheim Museum in Bilbao) heralds the start of the Passeig Marítim, which links the port with La Barceloneta and then extends 8km (5 miles) to Sant Adrià del Besòs.

➕ 121 F5 (Barceloneta)/121 F7 (Port Olímpic) 🍴 Plenty (€–€€€)
🚇 Barceloneta, Ciutadella/Vila Olímpica, Diagonal Mar 🚌 Barceloneta: 17, 36, 39, 40, 45, 57, 59, 64, 157. Port Olímpic: 10, 45, 57, 59, 71, 92, 157

MUSEU PICASSO

See pages 32–33.

MUSEU TÈXTIL I D'INDUMENTÀRIA

The Museu Tèxtil i d'Indumentària (Textile and Clothing Museum) acts as a reminder of how, thanks to its thriving textile industry, Barcelona rose to prosperity in the 1800s. It occupies a beautiful 14th-century palace, in what would then have been the aristocratic heart of Barcelona.

The museum collections include textiles, tapestries, lace and clothes from medieval to modern times, with displays of textile machinery, dolls, shoes and other fashion accessories.

www.museutextil.bcn.es

🔠 121 D5 ✉ Carrer Montcada 12–14 ☎ 93 319 76 03 🕓 Tue–Sat 10–6, Sun and public hols 10–3 🖐 Moderate 🍴 Café–restaurant (€) 🚇 Jaume I

PALAU DE MAR

Thanks to the influence of the Olympic Games, and the opening up of the old port as a leisure area, the Palau de Mar (Palace of the Sea) – an impressive late 19th-century warehouse – has been converted into offices, harbourside restaurants and the spectacular Museu d'Història de Catalunya (Museum of Catalan History).

This is one of Barcelona's most sophisticated museums, opened in 1996. Some critics have dubbed it a 'theme park', because of its lack of original exhibits, but it is nevertheless a dynamic and stimulating museum, covering the history of Catalonia in an entertaining fashion, through

state-of-the-art displays, films, special effects, interactive screens and hands-on exhibits – tread an Arab waterwheel, mount a cavalier's charger, drive an early tram, take cover in a Civil War air-raid shelter…

The museum is divided into eight sections, each presenting a thorough picture of the economy, politics, technology, culture and everyday life of Catalonia over the centuries: the region's prehistory, the consolidation of Catalonia in the Middle Ages, its maritime role, links with the Austrian Empire in the 16th and 17th centuries, its economic growth and industrialization, the 1936 Civil War and the ensuing repression of Catalonia under Franco, through to the restoration of democracy in 1979. The insight this innovative museum provides makes it easier for the visitor to understand the complexities of this 'nation within a nation'.

🚶 121 E5 ✉ Plaça Pau Vila 3, Port Vell ☎ 93 225 47 00 🕐 Tue–Sat 10–7, Wed 10–8, Sun and public hols 10–2.30 💰 Moderate; free 1st Sun of month 🍴 Rooftop café (€) 🚇 Barceloneta ❓ Gift shop, multimedia library, community programmes

PALAU DE LA MÚSICA CATALANA

In a city bursting with architectural wonders, the Palau de la Música Catalana (Palace of Catalan Music) – commissioned by the Orfeó Català (Catalan Musical Society) in 1904 and created by local architect Lluís Domènech i Montaner between 1905 and 1908 – stands out as one of Barcelona's greatest masterpieces and a symbol of the renaissance of Catalan culture. In 1997 it was declared a World Heritage Site by UNESCO.

The bare brick façade is highlighted with colourful ceramic pillars, fancy windows and busts of Palestrina, Bach, Beethoven and Wagner. The sculptural group projecting from the corner of the building represents popular song. A balcony runs around the building and the main structure is supported by ornate columns that form huge dramatic archways over the entrance.

The interior continues the ornamental theme with a profusion of decoration in the entrance hall, foyer and staircase – almost overpowering in its attention to detail. The *pièce de résistance*, however, must be the concert hall, with its exquisite roof (an inverted cupola made of stained glass), its sculptures, ceramics and paintings dedicated to musical muses (including Josep Anselm Clavé, the great 19th-century reviver of Catalan music), and its beautiful balconies and columns, designed to enhance the perspective of the auditorium.

It's no surprise that this is one of the city's main venues for classical music, and, until the restoration of the Liceu Opera House and the opening of the Auditorium, was home to two orchestras, the Liceu and the Orquestra Simfònica de Barcelona i Nacional de Catalunya. It's a memorable experience to attend one of the weekly concerts; the acoustics are as fine as the surroundings.

www.palaumusica.org

🕂 120 C4 ✉ Carrer Sant Francesc de Paula 2 ☎ 93 295 72 00
🕐 Daily 10–3.30 💰 Moderate 🍴 Café 🚇 Jaume 1, Urquinaona
❓ Entrance by guided tour only

PARC DE LA CIUTADELLA

This delightful walled park is a haven of shade and tranquillity just a stone's throw from the old city and waterfront. What's more, hidden among the trees, lawns, promenades and a boating lake, you'll find the Parc Zoològic and a host of other attractions.

In 1888 the park was the site of the Universal Exposition and still contains some impressive relics of that great fair, including a striking *Modernista* café which now houses the **Museu de Zoologia**, with highlights that include a fascinating Whale Room and a Sound Library of recordings of animal sounds. Nearby, the neoclassical **Museu de Geologia**, with its rare and valuable minerals, fossils and rocks, opened in 1878 as Barcelona's first public museum. The main showpiece of the park is the Font Monumental – a huge, neoclassical-style fountain, smothered in allegorical sculptures.

🚩 121 D6 ✉ Main entrance: Passeig Lluís Companys ✋ Free Ⓜ Ciutadella, Arc de Triomf, Barceloneta, Jaume I

Museu de Zoologia/Museu de Geologia

✉ Passeig de Picasso ☎ 93 319 69 12 (M de Zoologia); 93 319 68 95 (M de Geologia) ⏰ Tue–Sun 10–2 ✋ Moderate (joint ticket)

SANTA MARIA DEL MAR

See pages 40–41.

VILA OLÍMPICA

Just behind the Port Olímpic, the rundown district of Poble Nou was developed into the Vila Olímpica – home to 15,000 competitors during the 1992 Olympic Games. It is now a high-tech corridor of apartment blocks, shops and offices.

🚩 121 E7 ✉ Vila Olímpica Ⓜ Ciutadella 🚌 36, 41, 71, 92

The Eixample and Gràcia

At the heart of the Eixample is the famed 'Golden Square', an area of elegant streets lined with *Modernista* architecture ranging from private homes to public buildings, two of them by Gaudí: Casa Milà and Casa Batlló. This is also where you will find Gaudí's amazing unfinished La Sagrada Família, one of the city's most celebrated sights.

Gràcia, once an outlying village, is now a picturesque suburb. It is home to students, artists and writers and its atmosphere, narrow streets and shady squares contrast sharply with the orderly grid plan of fashionable Eixample. Gràcia also has a building by Gaudí – Casa Vicens.

CASA MILÀ

See pages 22–23.

L'EIXAMPLE

L'Eixample means 'The Extension' in Catalan, and this district was laid out between 1860 and 1920 to expand the city beyond the confines of its medieval walls and to link it with the outlying municipalities of Sants, Sarrià-Sant Gervasi and Gràcia.

The innovative plan, drawn up by liberal-minded civil engineer Ildefons Cerdà, broke completely with the tradition of Spanish urban planning, with its geometric grid of streets running parallel

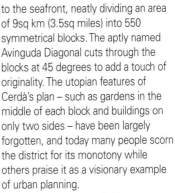

to the seafront, neatly dividing an area of 9sq km (3.5sq miles) into 550 symmetrical blocks. The aptly named Avinguda Diagonal cuts through the blocks at 45 degrees to add a touch of originality. The utopian features of Cerdà's plan – such as gardens in the middle of each block and buildings on only two sides – have been largely forgotten, and today many people scorn the district for its monotony while others praise it as a visionary example of urban planning.

The Eixample is divided into two *barris*, either side of Carrer Balmes. *L'Esquerra* (The Left) is largely residential and of less interest to visitors, whereas *La Dreta* (The Right) contains many of Barcelona's greatest *Modernista* landmarks, including Casa Milà, the three properties of La Manzana de la Discòrdia, the Fundació Antoni Tàpies, the Hospital de la Santa Creu i Sant Pau and La Sagrada Família. It is also a district of offices, banks and hotels. Chic boutiques and shops line its streets and, at night, Barcelona's smart set frequents its many restaurants, designer bars and nightclubs.

✚ 119 A7 🍽 Plenty (€–€€€) 🚇 Catalunya, Diagonal, Entença, Girona, Hospital Clinic, Passeig de Gràcia, Provença, Tetuan, Vergaguer, Universitat

FUNDACIÓ ANTONI TÀPIES

The Tàpies Foundation was established by Catalan artist Antoni
Tàpies in 1984 to promote the study and understanding of modern
art. It is housed in the former Montaner i Simon publishing house,
built by Lluis Domènech i Montaner between 1880 and 1889.
The striking *Mudejar*-style façade is crowned by an eye-catching
piece of art made of wire and tubing by Tàpies, entitled *Cloud and
Chair* (1990). Inside, there is an exhaustive library documenting art
and artists of the 20th century, and one of the most complete
collections of Tàpies' own works.

www.fundaciotapies.org

🞤 119 A8 ✉ Carrer d'Aragó 255 ☎ 93 487 03 15 🕑 Tue–Sun 10–8
✋ Moderate, children under 16 free 🚌 7, 16, 17, 20, 22, 24, 28, 43, 44
Ⓜ Passeig de Gràcia ❓ Library and small bookshop

GRÀCIA

In 1820, Gràcia was a mere village of about 2,500 inhabitants. By 1897, the population had swollen to 61,000, making it the ninth-largest city in Spain, known as a radical centre of Catalanism and anarchism. This is reflected in some street names – Mercat de la Llibertat and Plaça de la

Revolució. Since then, Gràcia has been engulfed by the expanding city, yet even now it maintains a village-like, no-frills, bohemian atmosphere and the *Graciencs* still call the cityfolk *Barcelonins*.

There are no real 'tourist' attractions here, except Gaudí's first major commission, Casa Vicens

(Carrer de les Carolines 24), still a private home. Gràcia's real appeal is its muddle of narrow atmospheric streets and squares, including the Plaça del Sol, an ideal place to stop for a coffee and watch the world go by. The Plaça de la Virreina and the Plaça de Rius i Taulet are two of the oldest squares. You'll also find a concentration of reasonably priced bars, restaurants and popular night venues in Gràcia.

➕ 117 E5 🍴 Plenty (€–€€€) 🚇 Fontana, Gràcia, Joanic, Plaça Molina ❓ *Festa Major* every August (▶ 11)

HOSPITAL DE LA SANTA CREU I SANT PAU

This remarkable hospital complex is a masterpiece of *Modernisme* by innovative architect Lluís Domènech i Montaner. Not only did he deliberately defy the orderliness of the Eixample by aligning the buildings at 45 degrees to the street grid, but he also built the complex in contradiction to established hospital concepts by creating a 'hospital-village' of 48 small pavilions connected by underground passages and surrounded by gardens, rather than one single massive building.

Construction began in 1902, as a long-overdue replacement for the old hospital in the Raval, following a bequest from a Catalan banker called Pau Gil. The new hospital was inaugurated in 1930. The main pavilion, with its graceful tower and ornate mosaic façade, serves as a majestic entrance to the whole ensemble. Inside, the various pavilions are grouped around gardens that occupy an area equivalent to nine blocks of the Eixample, where both doctors and patients alike can enjoy a peaceful natural environment. The pavilions are decorated in ornate *Modernista* style using brick, colourful ceramics and natural stone.

Over the years, the hospital complex has been restored several times and in 1984 it was declared a World Cultural Heritage site by UNESCO.

www.santpau.es

🕂 117 E8 ✉ Carrer de Sant Antoni Maria Claret 167–71 ☎ 93 291 90 00 🕙 Guided tours every half hour Sat–Sun 10–2 💵 Moderate; grounds free 🍴 Small coffee shop in one of the pavilions (€) 🚇 Hospital de Sant Pau ❓ Please remember that this is a hospital and not just a tourist attraction

MANZANA DE LA DISCORDIA

Casa Amatller

This is the first of three houses that have striking *Modernista* façades and are collectively known as the Manzana de la Discordia. Chocolate manufacturer Antonio Amatller i Costa commissioned Josep Puig i Cadafalch to remodel Casa Amatller into an extravagant home with a neo-Gothic façade decorated with sculptures, coats of arms and floral reliefs, and crowned by a stepped gable. Inside the broad entranceway, the beautiful wooden lift was one of Barcelona's earliest elevators. Note also the amazing carvings on one interior doorway depicting animals making chocolate. A combined ticket is available for a guided tour, *La Ruta del Modernisme*, which includes the three façades of Casa Amatller, Casa Batlló and Casa Lleó-Morera and discounted entry to attractions.

www.rutadelmodernisme.com

✚ 119 B8 ✉ Passeig de Gràcia 41 ☎ 93 488 01 39 ⏰ Mon–Sat 10–7, Sun 10–2 💷 Free 🚇 Passeig de Gràcia ❓ The entrance hall, open to the public, contains the information centre for *La Ruta del Modernisme*

Casa Batlló

Casa Batlló is one of the most famous buildings of the *Modernista* school, designed by Gaudí for Josep Batlló i Casanovas and completed in 1907. It is said to illustrate the triumph of Sant Jordi (St George) over the dragon, with its mosaic façade, covered in glazed blue, green and ochre ceramics, representing the scaly skin of the dragon, its knobbly roof the dragon's back, the tower the saint's cross and the wave-like balconies the skulls and bones of victims. A tour of the interior gives an insight into Gaudí's designs, and takes in an apartment, the attic and roof terrace.

www.casabatllo.es

✚ 119 B8 ✉ Passeig de Gràcia 43 ☎ 93 216 03 06/93 488 30 90
🕐 Daily 9–8; ticket office 9–1.30 💰 Expensive 🚇 Passeig de Gràcia

Casa Lleó-Morera

This striking building is considered Lluís Domènech i Montaner's most exuberant decorative work. Its flamboyant façade cleverly minimizes the corner by placing visual emphasis on ornate circular balconies, columned galleries and oriel windows. Inside, a florid pink mosaic vestibule and open staircase lead to first-floor living quarters, lavishly decorated with stencilled stuccowork, stained glass, marquetry and mosaics, portraying roses (the nationalist symbol of Catalonia), lions (*lleó*) and mulberry bushes (*morera*). It is closed to the public, but the exterior is well worth a visit.

✚ 119 B8 ✉ Passeig de Gràcia 35 ☎ No phone
🕐 Interior not open to the public 🚇 Passeig de Gràcia

PARC GÜELL

See pages 34–35.

PARC DEL LABERINT

These romantic, Italian-style gardens, on the wooded outer rim of Barcelona near the Vall d'Hebrón, present a pleasing contrast to the stark modern *espais urbans* (urban spaces) of the city centre. They originally surrounded a grand 18th-century mansion, which has long since been demolished, and are the oldest gardens in the city. The park has maintained its formal flowerbeds, canals and fountains, its ornamental statuary and its centrepiece – the 'Labyrinth' – a beautiful topiary maze with a statue of Eros at its centre. It is the maze that has given the park its name.

✚ 117 A8 (off map) ✉ Passeig dels Castanyers or Carrer Germans Desvalls, Vall d'Hebron ⏱ Daily 10 until dark, ticket office closes one hour before closing time ✋ Inexpensive; free Wed and Sun 🚇 Mundet 🚌 10, 27, 60, 73, 76, 85

PARC DEL CLOT

This park in the eastern suburbs has been built on the site of a disused railway yard and combines the walls and arches of the former rail buildings with a low-lying playing-field (the name 'Clot' in Catalan means 'hole') and a shady plaça, linked to a high grassy area of artificial hills and enigmatic sculptures by a lengthy overhead walkway.

➕ 121 B8 (off map) ✉ Carrer Escultors Claperós ⏰ May–Aug daily 10–9; Apr, Sep daily 10–8; Mar, Oct daily 10–7; Nov–Feb daily 10–6 ✋ Free 🚇 Clot, Glories

PARC DE LA CREUETA DEL COLL

This park was built in a disused quarry by Olympic architects Martorell and Mackay in 1987. Surrounded by dramatic cliff-faces, scattered with modern sculptures and embracing wooded pathways and a small sand-fringed boating lake, it serves the suburb of Vallcarca and is always packed in summer.

➕ 117 B5 ✉ Passeig Mare de Déu del Coll ⏰ Daily 10–sunset ✋ Free 🚌 25, 28, 87

LA SAGRADA FAMÍLIA

See pages 38–39.

Montjuïc to Sants

Montjuïc, a steep mountain to the south of the city, once had a Roman fort and temple to Jupiter crowning its heights. Since the 1929 International Exhibition, however, designer pavilions stand next to exhibition palaces, Olympic stadiums and concert halls.

One of the best ways to reach Montjuïc is by funicular railway, from the Avinguda Paral.lel Metro station. The Drassanes, the city's medieval shipyards which have been transformed into Barcelona's highly acclaimed Museu Marítim, lie to the east of Montjuïc at the port end of Las Ramblas, close to the station.

Once on Montjuïc, you'll find two of the city's greatest art museums, one dedicated to Joan Miró and his colourful works, the other showing a world-renowned collection of Catalan Romanesque frescoes that were rescued from decaying Pyrenean churches.

The Sants neighbourhood lies on the northern side of Montjuïc, and this is where you'll find Barcelona's main train station. Sants has been the scene for some interesting urban-development projects – instead of factories and workshops, outdoor art, spacious squares and friendly cafés await you, along with a pleasant laid-back atmosphere.

L'ANELLA OLÍMPICA

In 1992, Montjuïc was temporarily renamed 'Mount Olympus'
and became Barcelona's main venue for the Olympic Games.
Atop its western crest lies the Anella Olímpica (Olympic Ring),
a monumental complex of concrete and marble that contains
some of the city's most celebrated new buildings: Ricardo Bofills'
neo-classical sports university; the Institut Nacional de Educació
Fisica de Catalunya (INEFC); the Complex Esportiu Bernat
Picornell swimming-pool complex; Santiago Calatrava's space-age
communications tower, which dominates the skyline; and the
remarkable black steel and glass domed Palau de Sant Jordi,
designed by Japanese architect Arata Isozaki, which looks

more like a UFO than a covered sports stadium.

Barcelona had bid for the games three times previously and had built Europe's biggest stadium for the 1929 World Exhibition with the clear intention of using it for the 1936 'People's Olympics' (organized as an alternative to the infamous Berlin Games). These never took place due to the outbreak of Spanish Civil War the day before the official opening. For the 1992 games, local architects managed to preserve the stadium's original façade, while increasing the seating capacity from 25,000 to 70,000 by excavating deep into the interior. Highlights of the 1992 games can be relived through video clippings and souvenir showcases in the **Galería Olímpica**, located beneath the stadium.

🚩 118 D2 ✉ Avinguda de l'Estadi/Passeig Olímpic, Montjuïc ☎ Estadi Olímpic: 93 426 20 89; Palau Sant Jordi: 93 426 20 89; Picornell swimming pools: 93 423 4041 🚻 Free 🚇 Espanya, or Paral.lel, then Funicular de Montjuïc 🚌 61

Galería Olímpica ☎ 93 426 06 60 🕐 Apr–Sep Mon–Fri 10–2, 4–7; Oct–Mar by appointment for groups of more than 15 🚻 Inexpensive 🚌 61

FUNDACIÓ JOAN MIRÓ
See pages 26–27.

MONTJUÏC
See pages 28–29.

MUSEU NACIONAL D'ART DE CATALUNYA
See pages 30–31.

PARC DE L'ESPANYA INDUSTRIAL

With works by many Catalan artists, this is Barcelona's most controversial park – a *nou urbanisme* project, built between 1982 and 1985 on the site of an old textile factory. It is built on two levels, the lower part comprising a large lake and grassy area, with steep white steps up to the much-scorned upper esplanade, where there are ten lighthouses, a series of water spouts and an immense metal play-sculpture entitled the *Dragon of St George*.

✚ 118 A3 ✉ Carrer de Muntadas 🚇 Sants-Estació

PARC DE JOAN MIRÓ

Somewhat rundown these days, but enduringly popular, this park occupies an entire city block on what was formerly the site of a massive abattoir, hence its nickname Parc de l'Escorxador (slaughterhouse). It was created in the 1980s, and is always full of people reading, jogging,

dog-walking or playing *petanca* (boules) amid the attractive pergolas and orderly rows of shady palm trees. The park's most famous feature, however, is a startling sculpture 22m (72ft) high by Joan Miró, covered in multicoloured ceramic fragments, named *Dona i Ocell* (Woman and Bird).

✚ 118 B4 ✉ Carrer de Tarragona 🍴 Snack bar 🚇 Tarragona, Espanya 🚌 9, 13, 27, 30, 38, 50, 53, 56, 57, 65, 91, 109, 157

PAVELLÓ MIES VAN DER ROHE

Bauhaus architect Ludwig Mies van der Rohe created this masterpiece of modern rationalist design for the 1929 World Exhibition at Montjuïc, a construction of astonishing simplicity and finesse in marble, onyx, glass and chrome, widely acknowledged as one of the classic buildings of the 20th century. It was dismantled at the end of the fair and subsequently meticulously reconstructed and reopened (in its original location) in 1986, on the centenary of Mies van der Rohe's birth.

Inside, take time to enjoy the quality of the colours, textures and materials, as well as a striking bronze sculpture entitled *Der Morgen* (The Morning) and the famous 'Barcelona' chair, a design of timeless elegance created by Mies van der Rohe especially for the Expo, which has since been copied worldwide.

www.miesbcn.com

✚ 118 C3 ✉ Avinguda del Marquès de Comillas s/n ☎ 93 423 40 16 🕐 Daily 10–8 💶 Inexpensive 🚇 Espanya 🚌 27, 50, 91, 157

POBLE ESPANYOL

You can tour the whole of Spain in an afternoon here at Barcelona's 'Spanish Village', a remarkable showcase of regional architectural styles.

Built for the 1929 World Exhibition, the Poble Espanyol (Spanish Village) was intended as a re-creation of the diversity of Spanish regional architecture through the ages. The 115 life-sized reproductions of buildings, clustered around 6 squares and 3km (5 miles) of streets, form an authentic village, where visitors can identify famous or characteristic buildings ranging from the patios of Andalucia to Mallorcan mansions and the granite façades of Galicia.

Within the village are bars and restaurants serving regional specialities, and over 60 shops selling folk crafts and regional artefacts. Some are undeniably over-priced, but there are also some real finds. The Museum of Popular Arts, Industries and Traditions and the Museum of Graphic Arts are also located here and every Sunday at midday, a *festa* enlivens the main square.

The Poble Espanyol was smartened up for the 1992 Olympics, with the introduction of 'The Barcelona Experience' (a half-hour audiovisual history of the city), several restaurants and bars and El Tablao de Carmen, where you can see flamenco shows.

www.poble-espanyol.com

✚ 118 C3 ✉ Avinguda de Marqués de Comillas s/n
☎ 93 508 63 30 🕐 Mon 9am–8pm; Tue–Thu 9am–2am; Fri–Sat 9am–4am; Sun 9am–noon 💰 Expensive; free entry for wheelchair users 🍴 Plenty (€–€€) 🚇 Espanya
🚌 13, 50

Pedralbes and Tibidabo

**The city's efficient public transport will whisk
you to Barcelona's outlying districts and some
of its top destinations.**

In the western neighbourhood of Pedralbes sits the splendid
royal monastery of the same name, the perfect place to escape
the bustle of the city. South of the monastery, off the Avinguda
Diagonal, lies the Palau Reial de Pedralbes, a royal palace that now
houses a museum of ceramics and a museum of decorative arts.

The section of the Avinguda Diagonal
that cuts through the district of Les
Corts, between the Palau Reial de
Pedralbes and Plaça de Francesc
Macià, is lined with offices, banks
and apartment buildings, though
several modern mega-malls make it
a popular place with shoppers.

To the south is FC Barcelona's
stadium, Camp Nou, where football fans flock to see their team in
action. To the west are Barcelona's ultramodern science museum,
CosmoCaixa, and Tibidabo, where you can ride on roller-coasters
with the whole city laid out spectacularly before you.

MONESTIR DE PEDRALBES

The monastery of Pedralbes was founded by King Jaume II and Queen Elisenda de Montcada in 1326 to accommodate nuns of the St Clare of Assisi order. Following the king's death in 1327, Elisenda spent the last 37 years of her life here.

The spacious, three-storey cloisters – one of the architectural jewels of Barcelona – are still used by the Clarista nuns. Step inside and it is hard to believe you are just a short bus ride from frenetic downtown Barcelona. From here, there is access to the refectory, the chapter house and the Queen's grave. St Michael's Chapel is one of the highlights of a visit. It is decorated with remarkable murals by Spanish painter and miniaturist Ferrer Bassa

depicting Christ's Passion and the life of the Virgin Mary.

Monastic life in the 14th century is illustrated through permanent exhibitions in the original refectory, with its vaulted ceiling, the infirmary and the kitchens.

✚ 114 A2 ✉ Baixada de Monestir 9 ☎ 93 203 92 82 🕓 Monastery and museums: Tue–Sun 10–2. Closed Mon and public hols. Church: Tue–Sun 11–1 ✋ Moderate 🚌 22, 63, 64, 75 ❓ Bookshop, gift shop

MUSEU DEL FUTBOL CLUB BARCELONA

If you can't get a ticket to see one of Europe's top football teams in action, then at least visit the Barcelona Football Club Museum, the city's most visited museum after the Picasso Museum (➤ 32–33). Even those who loathe football can't help marvelling at the vast Nou Camp stadium, which seats over 98,000 spectators. The museum, under the terraces, presents a triumphant array of trophies, photographs and replays of highlights in

the club's history before leading you to the shop, where everyone can buy that essential club shirt, pen, scarf, badge, mug…

FC Barcelona, or Barça for short, is more than a football club. During the Franco era, it stood as a Catalan symbol around which people could rally, and this emotional identification still remains today. It also explains why this legendary club has the world's largest soccer club membership (over 112,000 members) and why the streets still erupt with ecstatic revellers following a win over arch-rivals, Real Madrid.

✚ 114 D1 ✉ Nou Camp – Entrance 7 or 9, Carrer Arístides Maillol ☎ 93 496 36 00 🕓 Mon–Sat 10–6, Sun 10–2 ✋ Moderate 🍴 Café (€) 🚇 Collblanc, Maria Cristina ❓ Gift shop

PALAU REIAL DE PEDRALBES

The Royal Palace of Pedralbes accommodated the Spanish Royal family during the International Exhibition of 1929. After 1939 it was used by Franco and then royalty and heads of state, before being opened to the public in 1960, along with the geometric gardens. Today the state rooms house two museums. The Museu de Ceràmica traces the development of Spanish ceramics from the 12th century onwards, and includes the 18th-century Catalan panels *La Cursa de Braus* (the Bullfight) and *La Xocolotada* (The Chocolate Party), together with works by Picasso and Miró. The Museu de les Arts Decoratives has an impressive collection of decorative arts from the early Middle Ages to the present day. Special emphasis is placed on 20th-century developments, from *Modernisme* to Functionalism and Minimalism.

www.museuartsdecoratives.bcn.es/**www.**museuceramica.bcn.es

➕ 114 C2 ✉ Avinguda de la Diagonal 686 ☎ Museu de les Arts Decoratives: 93 280 50 24. Museu de Ceràmica: 93 280 16 21 🕐 Tue–Sun 10–6 (park 10–sunset) 🎟 Museums: moderate, free 1st Sun of month. Park:

free 🚇 Palau Reial 🚌 7, 33, 67, 68, 74, 75 🛈 Shop, library, guided visits, educational services

TIBIDABO AND SERRA DE COLLSEROLA

Mont Tibidabo, 550m (1,800ft) high, forms the northwestern boundary of Barcelona and has panoramic views over the entire city, and, on exceptionally clear days, of Mallorca. The best views are from the **Torre de Collserola**, a telecommunications tower with a lookout point. At its summit, and topped by a huge statue of Christ, stands the modern Church of the Sacred Heart (Sagrat Cor). Near by, the **Parc d'Atraccions** cleverly balances traditional rides with high-tech attractions on several levels of the mountaintop, and is a fun day out for the family. Tibidabo is just one of the mountains of the Collserola range, a wonderful 6,550ha (16,200 arces) nature reserve with woodlands full of wildlife. It is best reached by FGC train to Baixador de Vallvidrera. From here, it is a 10-minute walk uphill to the **information centre**, where details of walks and cycles are available.

➕ 116 A3 (off map) 🖐 Inexpensive 🍽 Cafés (€–€€) 🚊 FGC Avinguda Tibidabo then Tramvia Blau to Plaça Doctor Andreu then by Tibidabo Funicular
Amusement Park ✉ Parc d'Atraccions del Tibidabo, Plaça Tibidabo 3–4 ☎ 93 211 79 42; **www**.tibidabo.es 🕐 Call for opening times or see website 🖐 Expensive 🚊 Funicular del Tibidabo
Information Centre ✉ Parc de Collserola ☎ 93 280 35 52 🕐 Daily 9.30–3. Closed public hols 🚊 Baixador de Vallvidrera
Torre de Collserola ☎ 93 406 93 54; **www**.torredecollserola 🕐 Wed–Sun 11–6

Excursions

Figueres	95
Girona	96–97
Drive: Alt Penedès	98–99
Montserrat	100–101
Penedès Wineries	102–103
Sitges	104–105
Tarragona	106–109

It would be a shame to visit Barcelona without also seeing something of Catalunya (Catalonia). Despite being an autonomous province of Spain, this region feels in many ways like a separate country, with its own language and traditions, culture and cuisine. Its geographical location makes it the gateway to Spain. Over time the passage of many peoples and civilizations has shaped the region, leaving cities such as Girona and Tarragona brimming with historical monuments, while its beautiful landscapes have provided inspiration for such artists as Gaudí, Miró, Dalí and Picasso.

The Catalan landscape is easy to tour and offers a wide variety of scenery, from the dramatic, snow-capped peaks of the Pyrenees and the secret bays and bustling fishing ports of the Costa Brava, north of Barcelona, to the acclaimed Penedès vineyards and long golden beaches of the Costa Daurada to the south.

FIGUERES

The main claim to fame of Figueres, two hours' drive northwest of Barcelona and 17km (10.5 miles) from the Franco-Spanish border, is that the great Surrealist painter Salvador Dalí was born here in 1904 and gave his first exhibition in the town when he was just 14. In 1974, he inaugurated his remarkable **Teatre-Museu Dalí**, located in the old municipal theatre, and to this day it remains one of the most visited museums in Spain. It is the only museum in Europe that is dedicated exclusively to his works.

The building, topped with a massive metallic dome and decorated with egg shapes, is original and spectacular – in keeping with Dalí's powerful personality. Its galleries are housed in a number of enclosed, circular tiers around a central stage and a courtyard containing a 'Rainy Cadillac' and a tower of car tyres crowned by a boat and an umbrella. The galleries contain paintings, sculptures, jewellery, drawings and other works from his private collection along with weird and wonderful constructions from different periods of his career, including a bed with fish tails, skeletal figures and even a complete life-sized orchestra. Dalí died in Figueres in 1989, leaving his entire estate to the Spanish State. His body lies behind a simple granite slab inside the museum.

🅸 Plaça del Sol ☎ 972 50 31 55 🍴 Plenty (€–€€)

Teatre-Museu Dalí

✉ Plaça Gala-Salvador Dalí 5 ☎ 972 67 75 00 🕓 Jul–Sep daily 9–7.45 Oct–Jun Tue–Sat 10.30–5.45. Closed 1 Jan and 25 Dec 🖐 Very expensive

GIRONA

Just 1.5 hours by car or train from Barcelona, the beautiful, walled city of Girona is one of Catalonia's most characterful cities, with an admirable collection of ancient monuments. The old city, built on a steep hill and known for its lovely stairways, arcaded streets and sunless alleys, is separated from modern Girona by the River Onyar. The medieval, multicoloured houses overhanging the river are a photographer's dream, especially when seen from the iron footbridge designed by Eiffel. Most of the main sights are in the old city. Make sure you also allow time to shop along the beautiful Rambla de la Llibertat and to enjoy a drink in the arcaded Plaça de la Independencia.

At the heart of the old city, centred around Carrer de la Força, El Call, the old Jewish quarter, is one of the best preserved in western Europe and is particularly atmospheric by night, with its street lanterns and intimate restaurants. Another splendid sight is the **Catedral**, with its impressive staircase leading up to a fine Baroque façade, a magnificent medieval interior and the widest Gothic vault in Europe. Housed inside a monastery, the **Museu Arqueològic** (Archaeological Musuem) outlines the city's history, and provides access to the Passeig Arqueològic, a panoramic walk around the walls of the old city. Near by, the 12th-century **Banys Arabs** (Arab Bath-house), probably designed by Moorish craftsmen following the Moors' occupation of Girona, is the best preserved of its kind in Spain after the Alhambra, particularly striking for its fusion of Arab and Romanesque styles.

🛈 Rambla de la Llibertat 1 ☎ 972 22 65 75 🍴 Plenty (€–€€)

Catedral

✉ Plaça de la Catedral ☎ 972 21 44 26 🕓 Tue–Sat 10–2, 4–7, Sun 10–2
🖐 Free

Museu Arqueològic

✉ Monestir Sant Pere de Galligans ☎ 972 20 26 32 🕓 Jun–Sep Tue–Fri
10.30–1.30, 4–7, Sat–Sun 10–2; Oct–May Tue–Fri 10–2, 4–6, Sat–Sun 10–4
🖐 Inexpensive

Banys Arabs

✉ Carrer Ferran Catolic ☎ 972 21 32 62 🕓 Summer Mon–Sat 10–7,
Sun 10–2; winter Mon–Sat 10–2 🖐 Inexpensive

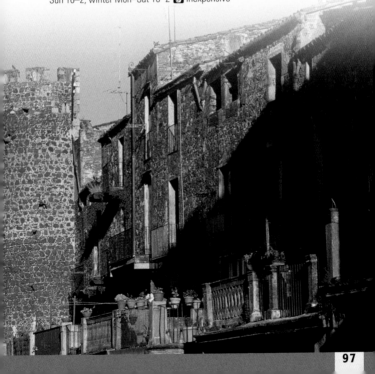

a drive

Alt Penedès

The main attraction of this drive is its magnificent scenery. Leave Vilafranca del Penedès on the BP2121 past Mas Tinell, Romagosa Torné and Torres wineries (► 102–103), until you reach Sant Martí Sarroca after 9km (5.5 miles).

This agricultural village contains an important Romanesque church with a splendid Gothic altarpiece, and a 9th-century castle.

Continue on to Torrelles de Foix, with its tiled church dome. The road then climbs through barren scrub up to Pontons. Continue up past the Romanesque church of Valldossera, through Els Ranxox, over the Coll de la Torreta, to Santes Creus.

Santes Creus, founded in 1158 alongside the Gaia river, is one of three exceptional former Cistercian monasteries in the region (the others are Poblet and Vallbona de les Monges). Following its deconsecration, it grew into a small village in 1843 when a group of families moved into the abandoned buildings and monks' residences.

Turn right at the main road (TP2002) to El Pont d'Armentera. Join the T213 to Igualada. After 22km (13.5 miles) of breathtaking mountain scenery, turn right to La Llacuna, then left through farmland to Mediona. Continue to Sant Pere Sacarrera then turn right at the main road to Sant Quinti de Mediona. Several kilometres later, turn left to Sant Pere de Riudebitlles.

Mediona is noted for its medieval church and ruined castle, while Sant Pere de Riudebitlles boasts a splendid Gothic manor house – the Palace of the Marquis of Lo.

The same road eventually leads to Sant Sadurní (➤ 102–103).

Distance 105km (65 miles)
Time 3–3.5 hours (without stops)
Start point Vilafranca del Penedès
End point Sant Sadurní d'Anoia
Lunch break Sant Jordi/Ca La Katy (€€) ✉ 8.5km (5 miles) outside Vilafranca del Penedès ☎ 93 899 13 26

Vilafranca del Penedès
🛈 Carrer Cort 14 ☎ 93 818 12 54 🍴 Plenty (€–€€)
Sant Martí Sarroca
🛈 Plaça de l'Ajuntament 1 ☎ 93 891 31 88
🍴 Limited (€€)

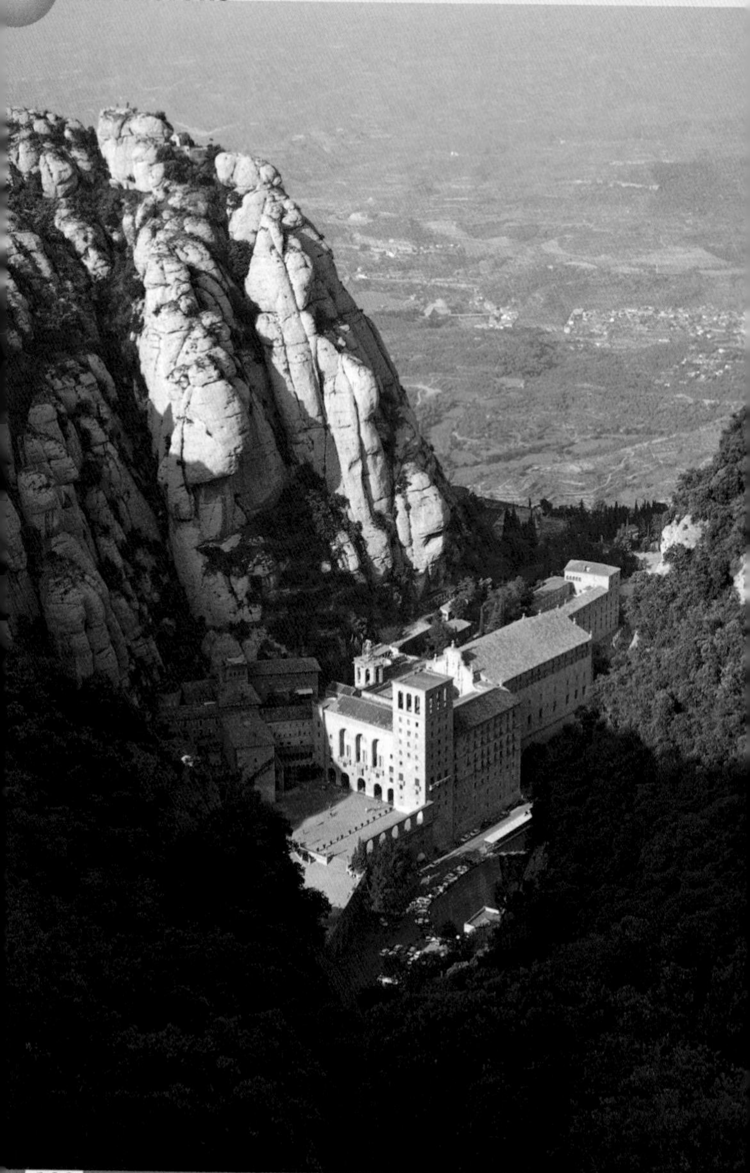

MONTSERRAT

Catalonia's holy mountain is 56km (35 miles) northwest of Barcelona with a summit of 1,200m (3,937ft). Montserrat is named after its strangely serrated rock formations (mont, mountain; serrat, sawed) and is one of the most important pilgrimage sites in the whole of Spain. Thousands travel here every year to venerate a medieval statue of the Madonna and Child called La Moreneta (The Black Virgin), blackened by the smoke of millions of candles over the centuries. The statue is said to have been made by St Luke and brought to the area by St Peter, and is displayed above the altar of the monastery church.

The spectacularly sited monastery, founded in 1025, is also famous for its choir, *La Escolania*, one of the oldest and best-known boys' choirs in Europe, dating from the 13th century. The choir sings daily at 1pm in the **Basilica**, a striking edifice containing important paintings including works by El Greco and Caravaggio.

Montserrat is clearly signposted by road from Barcelona, although the most enjoyable way to get there is by FGC train from Plaça d'Espanya, followed by a thrilling cable-car ride up to the monastery.

🛈 Plaça de la Creu, Montserrat ☎ 93 877 77 77 🍴 Limited choice of bars and restaurants

Basilica

✉ Monestir de Montserrat 🕐 Daily 7.30am–7.30pm subject to change

PENEDÈS WINERIES – VILAFRANCA AND SANT SADURNÍ D'ANOIA

The Alt Penedès is one of Spain's most respected wine-producing areas, producing Catalonia's best-known wines and all of its *cava* (sparkling wine). Since ancient times, viticulture has been the main economic activity of its two main towns, Sant Sadurní d'Anoia and Vilafranca del Penedès.

Only half an hour's drive from Barcelona, Sant Sadurní is the centre of Catalonia's *cava* industry, with 66 *cava* firms dotted throughout the town. The largest, Codorníu, produces around 40 million bottles a year and its magnificent *Modernista* plant is open to visitors daily. Tours last 90 minutes and include a tasting.

Near by, Vilafranca del Penedès, the region's capital town, has more character than Sant Sadurní, with its fine arcaded streets and medieval mansions. In the Gothic quarter, surrounded by squares, palaces and churches, the **Museu del Vi** is the only museum in Catalonia to be wholly dedicated to wine. Current methods of production can be observed at Vilafranca's three top wineries – **Mas Tinell, Romagosa Torné** and **Miguel Torres** – all outside the town centre on the BP2121 to Sant Martí Sarroca.

Museu del Vi

www.museudelvi.org

✉ Plaça Jaume I, 1 and 3, Vilafranca del Penedès ☎ 93 890 05 82 🕓 Jun–Aug Tue–Sat 10–9, Sun 10–2; Sep–May Tue–Sat 10–2, 4–7, Sun 10–2 ✋ Inexpensive

Penedès Wineries

☎ Codorníu: 93 818 32 32; Caves Romagosa Torné: 93 899 13 53; Mas Tinell: 93 817 05 86; Miguel Torres: 93 817 74 00 🕓 Opening times vary. Contact individual wineries for details

SITGES

Sitges, 40km (25 miles) south of Barcelona, is one of Spain's oldest bathing resorts and has long been the weekend and holiday playground of Barcelonans. It was once a sleepy fishing port and, although it has now developed into a thriving seaside destination, the old town still retains its ancient charm, with narrow streets, whitewashed cottages and flower-festooned balconies. It also has several appealing *Modernista* buildings.

It was artist and writer Santiago Rusinyol who first put Sitges on the map, bringing it to the attention of artists such as Manuel de Falla, Ramon Casas, Nonell, Utrillo and Picasso. Rusinyol's house, **Cau Ferrat**, is today a museum, containing works by El Greco and Picasso amongst others. Neighbouring **Museu Maricel de Mar** houses an interesting collection of medieval and baroque artefacts, and the nearby **Museu Romántic** provides a fascinating insight into 18th-century patrician life in Sitges.

Sitges is famous for its beautiful Platja d'Or (Golden Beach), which stretches southwards for 5km (3 miles) from the baroque church of Sant Bartomeu i Santa Tecla. Its palm-fringed promenade is dotted with beach bars, cafés and fish restaurants. However, the resort is perhaps best-known for its vibrant nightlife, drawing a young cosmopolitan crowd throughout the summer season. It is also a popular gay holiday destination. From October to May, Sitges is considerably quieter, except during *Carnaval* in mid-February when the town once more comes alive with wild parties and showy parades, drawing spectators from afar.

🛈 Carrer Sinia Morera 1 ☎ 93 894 50 04/ 93 894 42 51 🍴 Plenty (€–€€)

Museums

✉ Cau Ferrat and Maricel de Mar: Carrer Fonolar; Romántic: Casa Llopis, Carrer Sant Gaudenci 1
☎ Cau Ferrat: 93 894 03 64; Romántic: 93 894 29 69
🕐 Mid-Jun to mid-Sep Tue–Sun 10–2, 5–9; mid-Sep to mid-Jun Tue–Fri 10–1.30, 3–6.30, Sat 10–7, Sun 10–3
✋ Cau Ferrat: moderate. Maricel de Mar and Romántic: inexpensive. Combined ticket available for all three museums ❓ Romántic: guided tours every hour

TARRAGONA

This agreeable city is not very well-known to most foreign visitors to the region, even though it contains the largest ensemble of Roman remains in Spain, the remarkable architectural legacy of Roman Tarraco and was once capital of an area that covered half the Iberian peninsula. Originally settled by Iberians and then Carthaginians, it later became the base for the Roman conquest of Spain and the main commercial centre on this stretch of the coast until Barcelona and Valencia overshadowed it, after the Christian re-conquest of Spain in the early 12th century.

The town is sited on a rocky hill, sloping down to the sea. The ancient upper town contains most of the Roman ruins, some interesting museums and an attractive medieval quarter with a grand cathedral. Below the Old Town lies the modern shopping district, centred on the Rambla Nova with its smart boutiques and restaurants, and a daily fruit and vegetable market in Plaça Corsini. Below the main town, the chief attraction of the lower part of the city is the maritime district of El Serrallo with its colourful fishing fleet, traditional *Lonja* (fish auction), and dockside restaurants. The rocky coastline beyond conceals a couple of beaches, notably Platja Arrabassada and Platja Llarga.

Built into the hillside overlooking the Mediterranean, the **Amfiteatre Romà** (Roman Amphitheatre) was where the Romans held their public spectacles, including combats between gladiators and wild animals before an audience of some 12,000 people. During

the 12th century the Romanesque church of Santa Maria del
Miracle was built on the site, giving the beach below its name –
El Miracle. Tarragona's grandiose **Catedral** – a magnificent
Romanesque-Gothic building, in the form of a cross – was built as
the centrepiece of the ciutat antigua (old city).

The fascinating **Museu Arqueològic** (Archeological Museum)
includes a section of the old Roman wall, statues of emperors,

several sarcophagi and some interesting mosaics. Near by stands the Praetorium and the vaults of the first-century Roman Circus. The Praetorium is the site of the **Museu d'Història** (Tarragona History Museum), which traces the origins and history of the city through such treasures as the sarcophagus of Hipolitus, a masterpiece that was rescued from the sea in 1948.

Tarragona's most treasured Roman remains are housed in the **Museu i Necropolia Paleocristians** (Paleo-Christian Museum), in what was once an ancient necropolis, a 20-minute walk west of the city centre. It includes a valuable collection of mosaics, pottery, metalwork, glass and ivory. Currently closed for resoration.

For an overview of the old city and the hinterland of the Camp de Tarragona, walk the Passeig Arqueològic. This promenade encircles the northernmost half of the old town, around the Roman walls, of which 1km (0.5 miles) of the original 4km (2.5 miles) remains. Seven defence towers and gates still stand.

🚹 Carrer Major ☎ 977 24 52 03 🍴 Plenty (€–€€) ❓ You can visit the Amfiteatre, Passeig Arqueològic, Museu d'Història, Circ Romà and Casa Museu de Castellarnau on a combined ticket

Amfiteatre Romà

✉ Carrer Oleguer ☎ 977 24 25 79 🕒 Jul–Sep Tue–Sat 9–9, Sun 9–3; Apr–Jun Tue–Sat 10–1.30, 3.30–6.30, Sun 10–2; Oct–Mar Tue–Sat 10.30–1.30, 3.30–5.30, Sun 10–2 ✋ Moderate (combined ticket)

Catedral

✉ Plaça de la Seu ☎ 977 23 86 85 🕒 Summer Mon–Sat 10–1, 4–7; winter Mon–Sat 10–2

Museu Arqueològic and Museu d'Història

✉ Plaça del Rei ☎ 977 23 62 09 🕒 Museu Arqueològic: Tue–Sat 10–1, 4.30–7 (8 in summer), Sun 11–2. Museu d'Història: Tue–Sat 10–5.30, Sun 10–3 ✋ Moderate (combined ticket)

Museu i Necropolia Paleocristians

✉ Passeig de la Independència s/n ☎ 977 21 11 75 🕒 Currently closed for resoration. Check at tourist office

Index

air travel 12–13
airport 12
Alt Penedès 98–99
L'Anella Olímpica 82–83
L'Aquàrium 60
Arab Bathhouse 96

banks 17, 18
Banys Arabs 96
Barcelona Football Club Museum 89
Barcelona Museum of Contemporary Art 52–53
La Barceloneta 62–63
Barri Gòtic 45, 46–48
boat trips 14
Bus Turístic 14
buses 14

cable cars 15
Call, El (Girona) 96
Camp Nou 87, 89
car rental 15
Casa Amatller 76
Casa Batlló 76–77
Casa de la Ciutat 59
Casa Lleó-Morera 77
Casa Milà 22–23
Casa-Museu Gaudí 35
Casa Padellàs 54
Casa Vicens 73
Catalunya (Catalonia) 94–109
Catedral, Barcelona 24–25
Catedral, Girona 96
Catedral, Tarragona 108
Cau Ferrat 105
City History Museum 54
Ciutadella Park 68
Ciutat Vella 47
climate 8
clothing sizes 19
concessions 15
credit cards 18
crime and personal safety 19

currency and foreign exchange 18

Dalí, Salvador 95
dental services 9
Drassanes Reials 48–49
drink driving 13
drinking water 19
drive
   Alt Penedès 98–99
driving 8, 13, 15
drugs and medicines 19

L'Eixample 70–71
electricity 18
embassies and consulates 16
emergency telephone numbers 17

FC Barcelona 89
festivals and events 10–11
Figueres 95
Font Monumental 68
football 89
fuel 13
Fundació Antoni Tàpies 72
Fundació Joan Miró 26–27
funiculars 15

Galería Olímpica 83
Gaudí, Antoni 22, 34–35, 38–39, 55, 58
Girona 96–97
golondrinas 60
Gothic Quarter 45–48
Gràcia 69, 73
Great Royal Palace 57

health advice 8, 9, 18–19
Hospital de la Santa Creu i Sant Pau 74

IMAX Cinema 60
insurance 9
international dialling codes 17

King's Square 57

Magic Fountain 29
Manzana de la Discòrdia 76–77
Maremagnum 45, 60
Maritime Museum 48–49
Mercat de la Boqueria 50
La Mercè 48
metro 14
Mirador del Rei Martí 57
Miró, Joan 26–27, 84–85
Miró Foundation 26–27
Modernisme 55, 71, 74, 76–77, 90, 102, 104
Monestir de Pedralbes 88–89
money 18
Montjuïc 28–29
Montserrat 100–101
Monument a Colom 51
Museu Arqueològic, Barcelona 29
Museu Arqueològic, Girona 96
Museu Arqueològic, Tarragona 108–109
Museu d'Art Contemporani de Barcelona (MACBA) 52–53
Museu de les Arts Decoratives 90
Museu de Ceràmica 90
Museu Etnològic 29
Museu Frederic Marès 53
Museu del Futbol Club Barcelona 89
Museu de Geologia 68
Museu d'Història Catalunya 64–65
Museu d'Història de la Ciutat 54
Museu d'Història, Tarragona 109
Museu Maricel de Mar 105
Museu Marítim 48–49
Museu Militar 28, 29

Museu Nacional d'Art de Catalunya (MNAC) 30–31
Museu i Necropolia Paleocristians 109
Museu Picasso 32–33
Museu Romàntic 105
Museu Tèxtil i d'Indumentària 64
Museu del Vi 102
Museu de Zoologia 68
Museum of Catalan History 64–65
Museum of Drawings and Prints 31
Museum of Graphic Arts 86
Museum of Popular Arts, Industries and Traditions 86
museum opening hours 17

national holidays 11
National Museum of Catalan Art 30–31
Nitbus 14
Numismatic Museum of Catalonia 31

Old City 47
Old Port 60
Olympic Games 60, 68, 82–83
Olympic Ring 82–83
opening hours 17

Palace of Catalan Music 66–67
Palace of the Deputy 57
Palace of the Sea 64–65
Palau Güell 55
Palau de la Generalitat de Catalunya 59
Palau de Lloctinent 57
Palau del Mar 64–65
Palau de la Música Catalana 66–67
Palau Reial Major 57

Palau Reial de Pedralbes 90–91
Parc de la Ciutadella 68
Parc del Clot 80
Parc de la Creueta del Coll 80
Parc de l'Espanya Industrial 84
Parc Güell 34–35
Parc de Joan Miró 84–85
Parc del Laberint 79
Passeig Arqueològic, Tarragona 109
passports and visas 8
Pavelló Mies van der Rohe 85
Pedralbes district 87
pharmacies 19
Picasso, Pablo 32–33
Picasso Museum 32–33
Plaça de Catalunya 56
Plaça del Rei 57
Plaça Reial 58
Plaça Sant Jaume 59
Poble Espanyol 86
police 19
Port Olímpic 63
Port Vell 60
postal services 18
public transport 14–15

rail travel 13
Las Ramblas 36–37
Real Automóvil Club de España (RACE) 15
La Ribera 40
Royal Palace of Pedralbes 90–91
Royal Shipyards 48–49

La Sagrada Família 38–39
Sant Martí Sarroca 98, 99
Sant Pere de Riudebitlles 99
Sant Quintí de Mediona 99
Sant Sadurní d'Anoia 102
Santa Maria del Mar 40–41
Santes Creus 98–99

sardana 25
seat belts 13
senior citizens 15
Serra de Collserola 91
shopping 17
Spanish Village 86
speed limits 13
students/young travellers 15
sun protection 18–19

Tàpies Foundation 72
Tarragona 106–109
taxis 15
Teatre-Museu Dalí 95
telephones 16–17
Textile and Clothing Museum 64
Tibidabo 91
Tibidabo Amusement Park 91
time differences 9
tipping 18
tourist offices 9, 16
Town Hall 59
trains 14
Tramvia Blau 15
travelling to Barcelona 12–13

Vila Olímpica 68
Vilafranca del Penedès 102

websites 9
what's on when 10–11

youth hostels 15

Acknowledgements

The Automobile Association would like to thank the following photographers, companies and picture libraries for their assistance in the preparation of this book.

Abbreviations for the picture credits are as follows – (t) top; (b) bottom; (l) left; (r) right; (AA) AA World Travel Library.

4l Metro, AA/S L Day; **4c** Sagrada Familia, AA/P Wilson; **4r** Museu d'Historia de la Ciutat, AA/S L Day; **5l** Girona, AA/M Chaplow; **5c** Parc Guell, AA/M Jourdan; **5r** Las Ramblas, AA/P Enticknap; **6/7** Metro, AA/S L Day; **10** La Merce, AA/M Jourdan; **12/3** International airport in Barcelona, AA/S L Day; **14t** Metro sign, AA/M Jourdan; **14b** Bus, AA/S L Day; **15** Taxis, Port Olimpic, AA/S L Day; **16** Public telephone, AA/P Wilson; **20/1** Sagrada Familia, AA/P Wilson; **22** Casa Mila, AA/M Chaplow; **22/3** Casa Mila, AA/S L Day; **24** Cathedral, AA/ M Chaplow; **24/5** Cathedral, AA/S L Day; **25** Cathedral, AA/M Jourdan; **26/7** Fundacio Joan Miro, AA/S L Day; **28/9** View from Castle Montjuic, AA/M Jourdan; **29t** Montjuic, AA/M Jourdan; **29b** Placa de la Font Magica, AA/M Jourdan; **30** Museu Nacional d'Art de Catalunya, AA/M Jourdan; **30/1** Museu Nacional d'Art de Catalunya, AA/M Jourdan; **31** Museu Nacional d'Art de Catalunya, AA/M Jourdan; **32t** Museu Picasso, AA/M Chaplow; **32b** Museu Picasso, AA/P Wilson; **33** Museu Picasso, AA/M Chaplow; **34** Parc Guell, AA/S L Day; **34/5** Parc Guell, AA/M Jourdan; **35** Parc Guell, AA/M Jourdan; **36l** Las Ramblas, AA/S L Day; **36r** Las Ramblas, AA/S L Day; **37** Las Ramblas, AA/M Chaplow; **38** Passion Façade, Sagrada Familia, AA/M Jourdan; **38/9** Sagrada Familia, AA/M Jourdan; **39** Sagrada Familia, AA/P Wilson; **40** Santa Maria del Mar, AA/M Jourdan; **40/1** Santa Maria del Mar, AA/M Jourdan; **41** Santa Maria del Mar, AA/P Wilson; **42/3** Museu d'Historia de la Ciutat, AA/S L Day; **45** Las Ramblas, AA/M Jourdan; **46/7** Placa de Olles, AA/M Chaplow; **48** Musicians, AA/M Chaplow; **48/9** Drassanes and Museu Maritim, AA/M Jourdan; **50** Mercat de la Boqueria, AA/S McBride; **50/1** Columbus Monument, AA/S L Day; **52/3t** Museu Frederic Mares, AA/S L Day; **52/3b** Museu d'Art Contemporani de Barcelona, AA/M Jourdan; **54** Museu d'Historia de la Ciutat, AA/M Jourdan; **55** Palau Guell, AA/M Jourdan; **56/7** Placa de Catalunya, AA/S L Day; **57** Placa del Rei, AA/M Jourdan; **58** Placa Reial, AA/S L Day; **58/9** Placa Reial, AA/P Wilson; **59** Palau de la Generalitat, AA/S L Day; **60** Maremagnum, AA/M Jourdan; **61** La Ribera, AA/M Chaplow; **62/3** Arts Hotel, Port Olimpic, AA/M Chaplow; **63** Arts Hotel, Torre Mapfre, Port Olimpic, AA/M Chaplow; **64** Palau de Mar, AA/M Jourdan; **64/5** Palau de la Mar, AA/M Chaplow; **67** Palau de la Musica Catalana, AA/M Jourdan; **68** Parc de la Ciutadella, AA/S L Day; **69** Passeig de Gracia, AA/M Chaplow; **70/1** L'Eixample, AA/M Chaplow; **71** Farmacia Bolos, AA/M Chaplow; **72/3** Fundacio Antoni Tapies, AA/M Jourdan; **73t** Casa Vicens, AA/M Jourdan; **73b** Casa Vicens, AA/M Jourdan; **74** Hospital de la Santa Creu I Sant Pau, AA/M Jourdan; **75** Hospital de la Santa Creu I Sant Pau, AA/M Jourdan; **76** Casa Batllo, AA/S L Day; **77** Casa Lleo-Morera, AA/M Chaplow; **78/9** Parc del Laberint, AA/M Chaplow; **79** Parc del Laberint, AA/M Chaplow; **80** Parc del Clot, AA/M Chaplow; **81** Cable car, Montjuic, AA/S L Day; **82/3** Anella Olimpica, AA/M Chaplow; **83** Palau Sant Jordi, AA/S L Day; **84** Parc de Joan Miro, Dona i Ocell, AA/M Chaplow; **84/5** Parc de l'Espanya Industrial, AA/S L Day; **85** Pavello Mies van der Rohe, AA/M Jourdan; **86** Poble Espanyol, AA/M Jourdan; **87** Monestir de Pedralbes, AA/M Jourdan; **88** Panels, Monestir de Pedralbes, AA/M Jourdan; **88/9** Monestir de Pedralbes, AA/M Jourdan; **89** Museu del Futbol, Nou Camp Stadium, AA/M Chaplow; **90** Palau Reial de Pedralbes, AA/P Enticknap; **91** Parc d'Atraccions, AA/M Chaplow; **92/3** Girona, AA/M Chaplow; **95** Teatre-Museu Dali, AA/M Chaplow; **96** Girona, AA/M Chaplow; **96/7** Hostalric, Girona, AA/M Chaplow; **98/9** Santa Creus Monastery, isaifa Image Service s.r.o/Alamy; **100** Montserrat, AA/P Enticknap; **101** Black Virgin statue, Montserrat, AA/S Watkins; **102/3** Vilafranca de Penedes, AA/P Wilson; **104/5** Sitges, AA/S Watkins; **106** Tarragona, AA/P Enticknap; **107** Tarragona, AA/P Enticknap; **108/9** Cathedral, Tarragona, AA/P Enticknap; **125** Parc Guell, AA/M Jourdan; **126/7** Placa de Catalonia, AA/S Day; **128** The Hotel Arts at Port Olimpic, AA/M Chaplow.

Every effort has been made to trace the copyright holders, and we apologise in advance for any accidental errors. We would be happy to apply the corrections in the following edition of this publication.

Maps

★ Best places to see
■ Featured sight

☐ Las Ramblas & around

☐ La Ribera to Port Olímpic

☐ The Eixample & Gràcia

☐ Montjuïc to Sants

☐ Pedralbes & Tibidabo

0	500 m
0	600 yds

0	150 m
0	200 yds

Parc de la Creueta del Coll

PEDRALBES

Parc del Palau de Pedralbes

★ Park Güell

Parc del Turó del Putget

RONDA DEL GENERAL MITRE

114

GRAN VIA DE CARLES III

VIA AUGUSTA

Parc de Monterols

TRAVESSERA DE DALT

115 116

GRÀCIA

Parc de les Aigües

CARRER DE NUMÀNCIA

CARRER DE TARRAGONA

Jardins Poeta Eduard Marquina

AVINGUDA DIAGONAL

CARRER DE PARÍS

L'EIXAMPLE

CARRER DE BALMES

★ La Sagrada Família

CARRER DE LEPANT

CARRER DE PADILLA

★ Casa Milà (La Pedrera)

Parc de l'Espanya Industrial

SANTS

Parc de Joan Miró

CARRER DE ROSSELLÓ

CARRER D'ARAGÓ

CARRER DE LAIETANA

Parc de l'Estació del Nord

GRAN VIA DE LES CORTS CATALANES

AVINGUDA DEL PARAL·LEL

★ Museu Nacional d'Art de Catalunya

118

MONTJUÏC

Fundació Joan Miró

LAS RAMBLAS

119 120

EL RAVAL

Catedral ★

BARRI GÒTIC

122

LA RIBERA

Museu Picasso ■

121

Parc de la Ciutadella

CARRER DE LA MARINA

PASSEIG DE COLOM

Santa Maria del Mar

PORT VELL

BARCELONETA

PORT OLÍMPIC

RONDA LITORAL

113

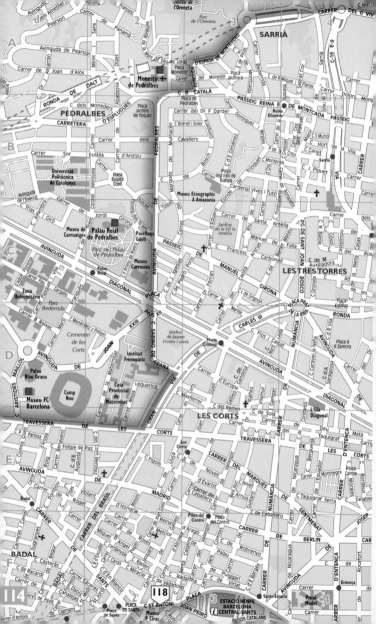

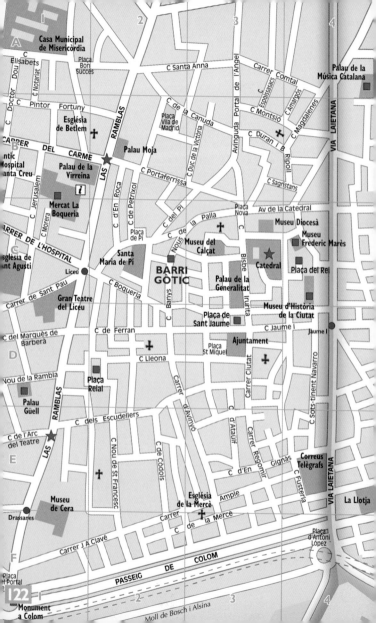

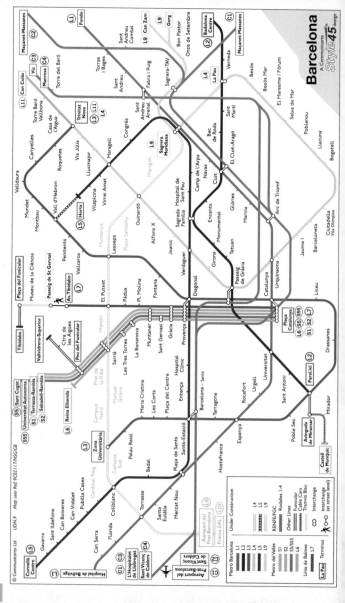

Barcelona

A Communicarta
style45 design

© Communicarta Ltd   UDN 9   Map uar Ref 9021 17/NSGGB